# A Canal Boy's Story

C.S. SIDAWAY

A Canal Boy
by Colin Sidaway

A catalogue card for this book is available from the British Library.

Paperback ISBN: 978-0-9955472-8-5

Ebook ISBN: 978-0-9955472-9-2

First published in 2018

Publication support

TJ INK
tjink.co.uk

Printed and bound in Great Britain by
TJ International, Padstow, Cornwall

# CHAPTER ONE

*Growing up on the canal*

My name's Jim James. I was born on the canal in the back cabin of our butty, *Ariadne*. I don't remember that, but everybody told me that was so. It didn't concern me particularly as all my peer group had all been born on the canal. My story started with my parents getting married. They jumped the broomstick and I don't think that they were ever churched, but Mr and Mrs Tom James were a respected couple. They were both from boating families and had never been to school or learnt to read or write, but you didn't need to read a book to be able to steer a canal narrowboat or shovel twenty tons of coal.

My earliest memory was probably being tied on to our horse, Bill. I think that I must have been about two. Being a two-year-old boy I must have been into all sorts of mischief in the eyes of my parents. Running around a canal lock, with the horse and ropes everywhere, I must have been a worry to them. So they tied me on the back of Bill. They knew where I was and wouldn't end up in the canal. That was up to the point where my younger brother, Bobby, was two and I was relegated to walking behind Bill while Mom and Dad worked the boat.

It was a hard life, not that we saw it like that as we didn't know differently. Mom did all the washing and cooking for three men, I include me in that, and all on a coal range in the back cabin. Looking back, I have no idea how she coped with all that and still helped Dad leg through Blisworth Tunnel while I walked Bill over the boat 'oss road with Bobby tied on his back.

Walking behind the horse on warm summer days seemed idyllic, but in winter with the short daylight hours I would walk through icy puddles, horse droppings and mud. There was no stepping around these hazards, you just walked on regardless. On rare occasions, such as on the sixteen-mile pound, Bobby and I would be tied on to the cabin top with

1

an old boot tied to the swingletree between the traces on the harness. Bill would hear the boot bumping along. Since the horse couldn't look round, he thought that somebody was still walking behind him. No boot bumping along, the horse would just stop. The boat would stem up and come to an embarrassing halt that resulted in Dad swearing at the top of his voice and cursing anything and everything. It was all a storm in a teacup. Once the boat had been righted and he had given Bill a slap on the backside, giving him the instruction 'Giddy-up, you bugger', our journey proceeded as if nothing had ever happened.

Up until the birth of Bobby, I slept on the side bed in the back cabin. I was then moved to a fore end cabin that Dad had put on. It reduced the amount of cargo we could carry but having a young expanding family, there was not much choice. When Bobby was about two, he was moved into the fore end cabin with me and we slept on two side beds. It was cold in winter, and I mean cold. Mom would come and dress us and take us to the back cabin where the coal-fired range provided the heat and we had Weetabix with hot condensed milk to give us some warmth. Dad would already be up and looking after Bill. Without Bill we weren't going anywhere. Dad really looked after the horse. He would bring his collar and blanket into the back cabin so that everything would be warm and dry to start the day. If the day was full of rain or snow, everything would soon become sodden and cold. The only thing that stopped the boats was the dreaded ice. Until the ice breaker went through, nobody was going anywhere. You knew when they were coming as you could hear the breaking ice a mile away. When the ice was broken, it became another working day except that it was unbelievably cold, and I only had short trousers, worn-out boots and socks with holes. Chilblains were caused from first being cold and then sudden warmth in the cabin. As Bobby and I grew, we helped Dad with the horse, brushing him down and making sure that he was fed and watered each and every day.

I remember I must have been about five when we were tied up at Brentford waiting for orders and Mom cajoled Dad into taking me to school. 'Jim must be about five now, and he needs to be a scollard and go to school to learn his letters and numbers.'

Dad had little or no choice. So, taking me by the hand, he took me to the single-room school where children off the boats were taken in for a few hours or a few days. As soon as we knocked the door and stepped inside, Dad removed his trilby and nervously pushed me forward.

The school teacher was a middle-aged lady with a bright red neck, I remember, and her hair tied back in a bun. A frustrated spinster if ever I saw one. You might think that a school mistress loved the children she taught. I doubt that she ever loved the motley group that she had the misfortune to have in her class.

'Yes, what can I do for you?' she demanded from Dad.

'It's young Jim, he needs schooling.'

'Off the boats, are you?'

'Yes, that's right, Miss.'

'Leave him here.'

'Yes, Miss,' and with that, Dad almost ran from the building. He was just glad to escape.

She grabbed me by the ear and twisted it. It was really painful. I hated school already!

'Now, young Jim, sit down there and I don't want to hear you. Just sit still and don't be a nuisance,' she told me, as she pulled me to a desk at the back of the class and sat me down.

She returned to the front of the class to try to get the day sorted. In front of me was another boy off the canal, a lad called Eddie. He turned round and gave me a cheeky grin. Miss Green, for that was the teacher's name, became furious and her red neck glowed blood-red. She had a wooden ruler in her hand and brought it down sharply on Eddie's head with such force that the ruler broke. Eddie was startled, with tears forming in his eyes.

'You, boy, sit and face the front. I don't want to see you look at anybody except me.'

In fear and trembling, I just sat wide-eyed in fear of my life. I was relieved when I heard a bell ringing and Miss Green made everybody stand up before dismissing us. I was so glad to get out and ran all the way back to the boat, where I was confronted by Mom.

'What are you doing here?' she asked.

'The bell went and everybody left the classroom.'

'So where are all the other children?'

I had no idea what she was talking about and looked around. There were no other children. I had left at mid-morning playtime break. Damn! Mom took me by the hand and walked me back to the school to push me into the classroom again. Once left alone with Miss Green, she made me hold out my hand and I had the benefit of another wooden ruler being brought down with unbelievable force. It stung like mad, but I wouldn't give her the satisfaction of thinking that she had hurt me and suppressed my tears. God, how I hated school!

At lunchtime, I was given a bottle of milk. That was my lunch, and I had to wait to go back inside the school room, impatiently waiting for the going-home-time bell. The afternoon dragged and I couldn't wait to leave.

Back at the boat, I was pleased that we had orders to collect a cargo from Regent Canal Dock, and I was no sooner back than we headed off along the canal, past Little Venice and the Maida Vale Tunnel, to tie up in the canal basin. Dad went off to look after Bill while Mom made dinner. I took a turn steering the butty. I had been to school and was well on the way to being a man, a boatman. I was barely five years old.

That wasn't the end of my schooling. Whenever we tied up for more than a day, I would be taken to the local school. It was the same story as and when I attended: I was put at the back of the class and told not to speak. I was seen and never heard. I learnt absolutely nothing. That didn't mean that I didn't know my letters. I would sit on the cabin roof with my slate and chalk and copied down the letters off the railway trucks as they rattled along beside the canal. I would write the letters down – LMS – and when we called in to Bulls Bridge or at the locks, the lock keeper would say, 'Morning, Jim. Have you done your letters?'

'Yes, Mr Mostrop,' I would say, proudly showing him my slate.

'That's right, Jim. That's correct. Very good.'

It put a smile on my face that I knew my letters, but I couldn't put them together to make words and thus be able to read. I was going to be a boatman and didn't need to read or write. I could steer a boat, groom a horse and put his harness on, and also work the locks. I would be a proud Number One.

From my earliest memories I had a special friend called Mary Lee. I don't remember a time when I didn't know Mary. It was mainly at weekends, when on Saturday nights all the boats tied up together near a canalside pub. The parents would go into the pub to drink beer. If we were lucky, we would have a bottle of lemonade or Vimto and a bag of Smith's crisps. We would just look through the windows as they had a sing-song and sometimes some men would do a step dance in clogs or hobnail boots while somebody played a melodeon. I would play with the other children. The girls joined in the games with the boys and played things like kick the can, which was a variation of hide and seek. All those who had been caught could be released if somebody could kick the can. The children's games were skipping and whipping a top or rolling a hoop. Group games were things like 'Opperley O', which was a variation of making choices and if you lost you had to go under the 'Wall of Death', where the unfortunate had to run through a barrage of punches from the others. Nobody really got hurt and I made sure that I very rarely lost.

Mary was special, and when we tied up near each other and it was pouring down with rain, we would go under the tarpaulins over the cargo and we would sit and talk about where we had been on the canal and how, one day, we would have our own boat. That was settled when I was about ten, when I stole a kiss. There was nothing for it, we would have to get married!

I didn't have Mary's favours to myself. There was another boy, Danny, who was a year older than me and had more experience with girls, or so I thought. I called him out one time when the boats were tied up on the same length. It resulted in a fight. I was angry and didn't want this boy anywhere near Mary. I got a bloody nose for my troubles. Neither of us won anything other than a few bruises. The next time I saw Mary, I told her that I didn't want her to see this Danny again. She just laughed at the thought that two boys were fighting over her.

When we were going through puberty we no longer sat under the tarpaulin, but we wrestled with each other. She would try to hit me. I would hold her wrist and wrestle with her on a grassy bank, trying to kiss her, and she would turn her head away so that I couldn't. Later, when we went back to our respective boats, she wished that she had let me and so did I.

Communication with Mary was difficult. The boats would pass each other going in opposite directions. I would jump up on the cabin top and wave my mop in her direction to get her attention. She would wave back.

'Where are you going?' I would ask.

'Banbury, with a load of DS. Where are you going?'

'Brum, with a load of spelter.'

'See you again soon.'

'Bye.'

It would be six or eight weeks before the boats were within a bike ride, so our romance was slow and fragmented. In my mind, we were betrothed and nothing would ever change that. How little I knew. It was later when we were teenagers that we went back to having a loving relationship, where we became more intimate under the tarpaulins or in the fore end cabin while parents were in the pub on a Saturday night. She was really loving and we became really intimate. She showed me what she liked, and part of that was pleasuring me. I wondered how she knew so much. Had she been with that other boy, Danny, or was it other boys? I never asked, and she never said.

Growing up on the canal meant that you lived close to nature and we were always hungry. Visiting the 'Garden of Eden' was an everyday event. In season, we would have apples, pears, plums and nuts. Dad always impressed on me: only take what you need, and leave something in case there was somebody who needed it more. I also learnt how to set a snare to catch a rabbit. I could also skin one and grill it over an open fire. To do this, I needed a knife; a sharp knife; my own knife.

I was nine or ten when I was shown how to make a knife by one of the older boys off the canal. We had a large extended family on both Mom's and Dad's side. It was Jeff who helped me make my knife. It was a piece of stainless steel sheet that was shaped and sharpened on a piece of sandstone. I made a handle by wrapping string around the blunt end. It was sometime later that I used it to make a sheath. I put a leather thong on the sheath so that I could fix the sheath and the knife to my forearm. I would never be parted from my knife. I used it to eat my food. I had seen Dad eat his dinner with his knife, collecting up all the gravy off the plate. He had used it for many years and the knife had been worn away so that it was more like a stiletto. If Dad could do that, so could I. It was just accepted. I was forever sharpening my knife until it was razor-sharp. A dull knife was no use to a boatman.

On special occasions, when we had been tied up for a couple of days, Dad had a .22 rifle. We would go out and he not only taught me how to shoot, but also how to catch a partridge or a pheasant and how to remove their feathers and draw them. My knife came in useful taking off the bird's head and claws. He was cross if I shot and missed. It was the waste of a shot, of which we had precious few, and we couldn't afford to waste one. I had to become a better shot and I did.

That boy, Danny, was not the only boy that I had a fight with. I had a run-in with a gypsy boy. I loved riding and sometimes the gypsies would tether their horses on the edge of the towpath. We were tied up early one night and near the adjacent bridge was a piebald gypsy pony. I looked around and couldn't see where the gypsies had set up camp. I released the pony and jumped up on his back. I kicked him on and had a gallop up and down the towpath, riding bareback. I had done this a few times and thought nothing of it. It was while I was re-tethering the pony that I realised that my riding had been noticed. There was a boy standing behind me and as I turned round he swung his fist and hit me. I retaliated, and the fight had started. To stop him throwing punches I bear-hugged him, and we fell not only to the ground, but into the canal. I released him and clambered out, totally soaked. I offered my hand to pull him out and we both stood on the towpath, looking at each other.

'I really like your horse,' I said to him.

'We're taking him to Appleby to sell him at the fair.'

'Don't know where that is. It's not on the canal. You should race him and you will get more money for him,' I suggested.

'You aren't a traveller, are you?' the boy asked.

'Sort of. I live on that canal boat over there,' I said, pointing out our boat.

'We could be sort of related,' he offered.

'What do you mean?'

'We could be blood brothers, but we have nothing to use as a knife.'

I released the strap on my knife and showed it to him. He was really impressed that I had actually made it.

'How do we become blood brothers?' I asked.

'You cut my thumb and I cut yours and we bind them together for a few minutes, and then we will be brothers for ever,' He said with a grin, and I noticed that I had knocked out one of his front teeth.

I offered him my hand and, without flinching, I let him cut the fleshy part of my thumb and then I returned the compliment by cutting his thumb. He took off his neckerchief and bound our thumbs together, and we sat down on the canal bank.

'I'm Jim James. What's your name?'

'Jonny Smith. Where do you go on your boat?'

'We get orders to carry cargo and load up, and the horse pulls the boat along to wherever we have to unload. We travel between London and Brum, and sometimes down to Oxford and up to Coventry. Where do you go?'

'Nowhere and everywhere. We sometimes go to Kent or over Worcester way picking fruit and hops, but in the spring we all meet up at a horse fair in Appleby. That's where me and Mom and Dad are going. It will take probably over a week.'

He undid his now-bloody neckerchief and I had a really messy bloody hand. We just went our own way.

Back at the boat, Dad was furious when he saw what would be a scar on my thumb. He took my knife and looked at it. It was still covered in blood and he thought that I had been in a knife fight. He cuffed me around my head.

'I don't ever want to hear that you have been fighting with knives. If you do it again, I'll take the knife off you.'

I didn't correct him. I just took my knife back and returned it to its sheath. He went and found some Dettol and found a piece of rag, doused it in the Dettol and wrapped up my thumb. A few days later, I removed the dressing and admired my scar. Jonny Smith and his horse had disappeared and I didn't see him again.

I was about twelve, I suppose, when Bill had to be sent to the knacker's yard. We had a choice to make. Do we get another horse, or get a motor boat and work a pair of boats rather than just one? There would be bigger payloads having two boats and having two boys to help, we would have a better lifestyle and more space, as we were getting too big to share the fore end cabin on the *Ariadne*. So it was decided that we bought a motor boat, *Leo*. It started my love of diesel engines. I would spend hours cleaning it and polishing all the brass parts. I just loved that two-cylinder National. When it was serviced at the depot, I spent every minute watching what the mechanic did and I was full of questions so that I understood, and by the time I was fifteen I could do the service myself. It saved Dad the cost of carrying out the service.

Our clothes were always mend-and-make-do. One day, we were on our way to Sampson Road Wharf in Birmingham when I noticed in a field that the scarecrow had a hat and jacket that looked better than mine. I gave the helm of *Leo* to Bobby and at the next bridge jumped off and skirted the hedgerows back to the field, where I did a swap with the scarecrow with his hat and jacket. I ran back to the canal to try to catch up with the boats. I caught up with them at the next lock. I was accosted by Dad.

'Where did you slope off to? We wanted you to set the road for us and I saw you running off over the bridge.'

'I saw a scarecrow and gave him a change of clothes. He had a better hat and jacket than me, so I did a swap.'

The hat didn't really fit, but a hat was a hat. I didn't know what Dad's response would be.

'Next time, find a hat and jacket for me. Now, get that windlass out and get these boats moving.'

I ran off to see where Bobby had got to with the lock, to help him. I never heard about the incident again.

It was while we were tied up at Bulls Bridge that my life was changed forever. It came as a great shock.

# CHAPTER TWO

*How not to join the army*

We had been tied up for just a day when I heard my name on the tannoy.

'Would Jim James report to the office? Thank you.'

That had never happened before, and I wondered why Mr Mostrop wanted to see me. I knocked on his door and went in.

'Morning, Jim. I've got a letter here for you.'

I had never had a letter, and was now almost frightened at the thought that Mr Mostrop had an envelope in his hand, offering it to me. I backed away.

'Take it, lad. It won't bite you.'

I just shook my head. I was afraid of something that I knew nothing about.

'Don't tell me you can't read. Well, you aren't the first and I don't suppose you will be the last. Do you want me to read it to you?'

I just nodded.

Mr Mostrop opened the envelope and read the letter. He put it all back in the envelope. 'It's your call-up papers.'

'What does that mean?'

'You have to go to Catterick as soon as possible, and go and tell them that you can't read or write and they will send you back here.'

'I don't want to go,' I stammered.

'Jim, if you don't go, the police will come down here to find you, arrest you and send you to prison and then make you do your National Service. It's best if you go.'

'Where do I have to go?' I asked.

'You register at Catterick Garrison. To get there you need to go to the King's Cross railway station. You know where that is, it's near Camden Lock.'

I nodded. I had passed the station many times going to and from

Regent Canal Dock.

Mr Mostrop continued his instructions. 'Go to the station. Show them this letter and they will give you a ticket and tell you what train to catch, and you need to look out for the station.'

'Is it a long way away?'

'It's in North Yorkshire, and it will be something like a six-hour train ride.'

He gave me the envelope, which I put in my jacket pocket.

'Give your dad this order. It's for picking up limes in Regent Canal Dock. They need to be delivered to the Jam 'Ole.'

'Right, Mr Mostrop, I'll give him the order and he can drop me off at Camden Lock.'

I walked slowly back to the boat, where Dad was waiting for me.

'Well, son, what did Mr Mostrop want?'

'I've had my call-up papers. I have to go straight away to a place called Catterick.'

He took the news thoughtfully. There would be implications if I was away for two years. Who would help run the boats and help unloading? Maybe I would come back when I failed my medical, as I wouldn't be able to read or write.

Mom was upset, but Dad reassured her. 'If Jim's accepted, he will go a boy and come back a man.'

I guess Dad would always be proud of me. I handed him the order to pick up the cargo of limes. We would go the following morning. I would have just one last meal on the boat with us as a family.

We were on our way just after five in the morning. I didn't really know the time, but we always had early starts. The alarm was set at 4.10. That's what I had been told for as long as I could remember. It meant that we tied up at Camden Lock and I had no packing. I went with the clothes I stood up in. I had nothing. I left my overcoat for Bobby. I reckoned I would be back and if I wasn't, the army would give me a replacement.

Dad walked with me into the station. I had never been in such a large building. There seemed to be people everywhere. I had never seen so many people all in one place before. I nervously gripped Dad's arm. We saw two soldiers and Dad went and asked them what I needed to do. They pointed me towards the ticket office, where I produced my letter and they handed me a ticket. Dad asked a porter what train I needed to get to go to Catterick. It was a semi-fast. Fast up to York, and then stopping everywhere before reaching Newcastle.

I said goodbye to Dad, found a compartment and sat by the window. Dad didn't stay and went back to the boats. He had a load to pick up. I sat alone in the compartment, before other people came and joined me. The train lurched out of the station and soon the telegraph poles were flying by. I had never travelled so fast in all my life. I was really on edge and apprehensive about everything and everybody. At each and every stop, I asked if it was Catterick. It wasn't. I had to stay on the train.

The ticket collector came and looked at my ticket. He punched it and gave it back to me. He recognised the signs of a young lad off to do his National Service. I asked if he could tell me when to get off, and he said that he would make sure that I got off at Catterick.

The hours passed, the stations along the way came and went. It was now getting dark and when the guard finally told me that this was Catterick, the train was almost devoid of passengers. It was dark outside, cold and raining. Welcome to North Yorkshire.

I stood on the platform as the train pulled out. I had no idea where I was or which way I needed to go. There was a light on in the waiting room and a fire. I went in there, wondering what to do. I would wait until first light and then find out where to go.

I was prepared to settle down for the night when two policemen came in.

'Eh, you. You can't stay here.'

I just sat up and looked at them.

'I don't think that he has any means of support,' one said to the other.

'What's your name?'

'Jim, Jim James.'

'Do you have any identification?'

'I've only got this letter,' I said, handing it to them.

They looked at the letter.

'You're two days early. Where have you come from?'

'Bulls Bridge.'

'Never heard of the place.'

I gave them my ticket.

'You've come up from London.'

'King's Cross.'

'Do you have any money?'

I shook my head. I then realised that they were Transport Police.

'You aren't real police. You work for the Transport. We have you guys down at Brentford, on the canal.'

'What do you know about them? You haven't been in trouble, have you?'

'No, I was born on the canal and work the boats with my Mom and Dad. The Transport Police never bother us. I think that they are mainly concerned with people off the bank doing damage and throwing things in the cut.'

'Well, son, you can't stay here.'

I made no response. I didn't know where to go.

'Tell me, son, when did you last have a meal?'

'I had breakfast this morning. I had a piece of dip with brown sauce and a mug of tea.'

The police looked at each other.

'Turning this lad out tonight, he is likely to catch pneumonia and wouldn't be use to anybody, including the army. We could take him back and put him in one of the cells tonight.'

'Aye, let's do that. Come on, young fella. You come with us.'

I walked out with them to where they were stationed. They gave me a mug of hot sweet tea and a bread and butter sandwich. I settled down on a bunk in one of the cells and they threw me a blanket. I slept warm and dry.

I awoke early, wondering where I was. I folded up the blanket and left it on the bunk bed, only to find that I was in a police cell. I was met by one of the Transport policemen.

'Ah, the sleeper awakes. Are you alright?' he asked.

'Yes, thanks, and thank you for the tea last night.'

He found me a mug and gave me another hot drink and also a piece of toast. I warmed my hands on the side of the mug, after I had stuffed the toast in my mouth.

'Give me a few minutes and I'll take you to the registering area in the garrison.'

I just sat in the waiting area and patiently waited. Eventually he came back with his overcoat on. I reckoned it was cold outside, and it was. It was a fair walk to the gatehouse of the garrison, and he led me into where the Army Police unit were housed.

'I've got another one for you,' he announced. 'Found him loitering on the railway station last night. He's already had a night in the cells.'

'Thanks. You can leave him here. We'll take him to where he needs to be. I take it that he has no ID?'

'Only this letter telling him to be here. He says he can't read or write.'

'He won't be the only one claiming that, but the team will sort them all out.'

The Transport policeman left, leaving me in the guardhouse. 'Come with me,' said the Army policeman as he put on his red cap.

I followed, trying to keep up as we marched to an adjacent building where the induction was taking place. There were only a few people there. I was two days early.

I was left facing a man sitting at a desk. He never raised his head but was filling out papers on his desk.

'Name?' he asked.

'Jim.'

'Not that name, your other name,' he said, getting irritated with me.

'James.'

'Not that name, your other name.'

'That is my name: Jim James.'

'Are you trying to be funny?'

'No, I'm just giving you my name.'

He looked up and then away to his colleagues. 'We've got another one here. It's probably a day for them. So, Jim James,' he said, as he looked at the letter I had received, 'go and see that man over there.'

I looked to where he was pointing and saw a man in a white overall. I went to see him and gave him my form.

'Just stand there,' the man said.

I duly complied.

'Can you see the letters on that chart?'

'Yes, I know my letters.'

'Good. Which ones can you see?'

14

'All of them.'

'Read the letters off the bottom line.'

'There's a snake – that's an "S". The next is a little mountain – it's an "A". The next is round – it's an "O"...'

'OK, that's enough. Don't strain your brain, the army might need it. Open your mouth.'

I did, and he put a thin piece of wood on my tongue, holding it down. It was all very strange.

'Go and sit down behind that screen.'

I went round and sat down. He stood behind me and clapped his hands.

'Did you hear that?' he asked.

'Yes.'

'Which ear was loudest?'

'This one.' I pointed to one.

He then repeated it with the other.

'There's nothing wrong with your hearing,' he said, as he wrote on my form before giving it back to me. 'Go through that door to see the MO.'

I had no idea what an MO was. I found out that he was an army doctor. It was another man wearing a white coat.

'Take off all your clothes and leave them there,' he said, pointing to a shelf.

I wasn't happy about undressing and I didn't want him to see my knife. I removed my shoes first and palmed my knife and sheath into one of the shoes, and kept it in place by stuffing my socks in the shoe. I then stripped off.

He put two tubes into his ears and with the other end he put it on my chest, before tapping me in a couple of places. He then turned me round and I then felt him touch a few places on my back.

'Turn round.'

I duly turned round, and he put his hands under my privates!

'Cough.'

I coughed.

'There's nothing wrong with you. A1.'

I just stood there wondering what to do, and was self-conscious not wearing any clothes.

'Take your clothes and this form through there,' he said, pointing to yet another door.

I collected my clothes and went into an office where there were several desks with men sitting there, waiting for something to happen or somebody to process. I presented myself to the first and gave him the form.

'What have you got to tell me?' he asked.

'I can't read or write,' I explained.

'You and a few hundred others.' He turned away from me to look at his colleagues. 'Here's another one. I will sort him out.'

He found a large piece of paper with lots of writing on it.

'Read this and sign here,' he said, pointing to a space on the bottom of page.

'I can't read it. What does it say?'

'Just sign here,' he insisted. It was a test that I didn't understand. I was signing on for five years. National Service was for just two years. If I could read the form, I wouldn't sign, but I couldn't and just did as he asked. I made my mark.

He burst out laughing. 'He's only put his cross on this,' he announced to his colleagues, who all started laughing. I couldn't see the joke. He turned to me. 'That's very clever. I've not seen that before but, young man, I'm accepting your mark as your signature and welcome you to the army.'

I didn't understand how I had been tricked and was now in the army, when I should be going back to Mom and Dad, working on the canal.

'Off you go. Through there to see the sergeant, who will kit you out.'

I took all my clothes and went into a large warehouse. The sergeant looked bored. He was smoking a cigarette. He reluctantly put it down and out.

'I suppose you want to be kitted out.' He looked me over and went into the warehouse, and returned with two of nearly everything.

'Shoe size?' he asked.

'No idea.' I had never realised that shoes had sizes, they either fit or they didn't.

He picked up one of my shoes. 'Nine.' He came back with a pair of brand-new boots and a pair of ordinary shoes.

'Leave your civvy things here and put on these.'

I started with a pair of shorts. I had never had any shorts before, and was amused that there was a flap at the front for me to pee through. I put everything on and palmed my knife from my shoe to the new shoes. I put on my boots. They were hard and unworn. I would need to soften them up.

A corporal was watching me, smiling as I put the boots on. 'If you don't wear socks you will get blisters and then you will be on a charge.'

He must have seen this many, many times and I was just another raw recruit, and I guessed that he would use his authority to try to bully me and all the other recruits.

I paid little or no attention as I struggled with the boots.

'Pick up your things and come with me,' he gave out his instructions. I didn't understand why I wasn't going back to the boats. Somehow, nobody believed me when I told them that I couldn't read or write. I reluctantly followed him to a timber hut that was full of beds. There were two other men already there. They stood up as he marched in.

'Choose a bed and these two will tell you where you can collect your bedding. I'll be back later. It will be lights out at nine o'clock, and that means that you go to bed and don't wonder around outside. Reveille is at six in the morning, that's your early morning alarm call.'

He strutted up and down the centre of the hut between the beds.

'You see these two stripes, it means that I'm your corporal. When you see me you have to salute me. Men with three stripes are sergeants and you need to salute them. The others that wear caps are officers and everybody salutes them. So, let me see you salute.'

I had no idea what he was talking about, but the other two gave him a salute that didn't please him and I was just looking at him.

'You've been looking at too many American films, and what are you looking at?' he asked me.

'I was just looking at your uniform so that I would recognise it next time.'

'You didn't salute me,' he complained.

'I didn't know what you meant, but can I try?'

'Please, that would be very nice,' he said facetiously.

I stood to attention and gave an almost perfect salute.

'I thought you said that you didn't know about saluting?'

'I saw some army men do that when I was little and wondered what they were doing.'

'Well, now you know. You can show these two and you can practise in your own time.'

With that, he turned and walked out. The other guys came and introduced themselves, they were Paul and Andy. I told them that the corporal was likely to pick on me. They tried to reassure me and came with me to the stores, where I collected my bedding and returned to the hut. Lunchtime came around and the boys went with me to the mess, where a hot meal was being served. They piled up their plates with as much as they could. I just took a few potatoes and a piece of meat that looked like beef – I would never know, as we had never had beef and gravy. I also took a piece of bread. We sat together. I collected just a knife and started eating with just that, looking at how they used their fork. I had never had a fork. I mopped up the gravy with the bread. I had never had a cooked meal in the middle of the day, except Sunday when Dad managed to catch a rabbit.

Walking back to the hut we passed two men in caps. They must be officers, so we all saluted them, so that they were acknowledged. It felt right.

Back in the hut, the boys showed me how to make my bed. It seemed easy. What I really needed was a bowl. If I soaked my boots overnight in urine, that would soften them up, and then wearing them for a day while wet would mould the boots to my feet and I wouldn't have a problem with blisters.

I asked, 'Do you have a dipper, or know where I can borrow one?'

'What the hell's a dipper?'

'If you have never heard of one, you certainly haven't got one.' It was a hand bowl that was always hung up in the boat cabin by the hatches.

I realised that I would have to find my own. It was time to have a scout around. I found myself at the back of the mess, where there was a sort of dump, and I found a colander and the end of a roll of silver paper. That would do. I could make a dipper with that and returned to the hut. I took the colander and silver paper to make an improvised bowl. I peed into the bowl and over my boots. I really needed more urine and thought of asking the lads to oblige, but decided against it in case they thought I was a pervert or something. I put the bowl behind the sign outside the hut. Nobody would look for it there. I would pee in the bowl again later.

I went with Paul and Andy to the mess for another meal. They seemed to eat enormous meals that were mainly potatoes. I only had what I thought I needed, which was not very much by comparison.

We had just returned to the hut when the corporal brought in another recruit, who seemed rather effeminate. I guessed that he would have a good time in the army, providing he didn't make it too obvious. The corporal had another victim for his ire, but he turned to me.

'Saw you salute top brass today. Very good, but what were you doing around the back of the mess kitchen?'

'Looking for a dipper,' I simply replied.

'Did you find one?'

'No, I only found an old colander.'

'Don't let me catch you ferreting around there again. Let me see you make your beds. Chop-chop, get on with it.'

I remembered how Paul and Andy had shown me how to make the bed, and set about putting the sheet and blanket on, smoothing down the bed when I had finished. I then stood to attention at the foot of the bed.

'Ah, we have somebody who thinks that he's made his bed,' the corporal said, as he pulled the blankets and sheets off leaving them in a heap on the floor. 'Make the bed again.'

I guessed that this was the army way. Kill the spirit and obey orders so that when ordered to, you would lay down your life. I just stripped everything off the bed, neatly folding it before remaking it. By the time I had finished I was last.

'So, you think you have made your bed,' he said, and threw the covers off again. He was making an example of me. 'Who made your bed at home? Are you a mommy's boy?'

'No, Corporal. I've never slept in a bed. I only had a bunk on the boat.'

'Oh, you lived on a boat. Was it a luxury yacht?'

'No, a canal boat on the Grand Union Canal.'

He came and put his face only a few inches from mine. 'Don't try to be funny or clever with me. I've sussed you out. You are a troublemaker. Don't even think of anything except what I tell you to think.'

'No, Corporal.'

'Are you being insolent?'

'I don't know what that is.'

'You, soldier, had better watch your step. Now, you can stand there and only make your bed after lights out, and the rest of you take note and don't help him.'

He turned and left. I guessed that he would have a good laugh at my expense in the corporals' mess later when he told his story. I would get my revenge in my own time, when the opportunity came round. It gave me something to think about while just standing there. I reckoned that he would eventually trip up over his own tongue.

It must have been just before nine o'clock that he came back to the hut, to see me standing there exactly in the same place as when he left. I thought that he was disappointed in one way and couldn't give me another tongue lashing, but satisfied that he had exerted his authority over me.

'Right, you lot. When I come in, I want you to stop whatever you are doing and stand at the foot of your bed. Have you all got that? Good. Tomorrow you need to be up with reveille, ready for the day. Nothing happens here until we have the rest of you rabble on Monday, and Tuesday you start your basic. In the meantime, I want you to clean your kit, polish your brass buttons and badges, and I want to see my face in your boots.'

With that he turned round and left. I guessed that he would be outside just watching. I was right; he was gone not two minutes when he put his head round the door, hoping to catch me having moved. He was unlucky. I was still standing in the same spot. He was determined to catch me out, and I was on to him and was equally determined not to be caught out through his petty ways.

Suddenly the lights went out. In the dark, I remade the bed, not that I was going to sleep in it. I found my great coat and put it on. I thought of going out the front door but decided against that, as I expected the corporal to wait to see if anybody came out. I climbed out the window at the far end of the hut. I needed somewhere to sleep. It wouldn't be in the hut nor in the bed. I found a quiet corner in a lean-to that housed a heating boiler. This would do very nicely. I put down some newspaper that the boiler man had left and curled up on the floor. I slept.

I was awake with the dawn. The camp was quiet with nobody about. I got up and found the latrines and had a wash in there. I then walked to the back of the mess to the kitchen area. There was a squaddie smoking a cigarette.

'Any chance of a cup of tea?' I asked.

'Need to ask the sergeant,' he said, moving his head to direct me in the right direction.

I went into the kitchen and found the sergeant sitting at a desk going through some papers. I stood to attention and saluted him. He looked up in surprise at my appearance.

'What the hell do you want at this time in the morning?' he asked.

'A cup of tea, please.'

'A cup of tea! Gawd love us. It's just coming up to five. Don't tell me you are one of the new blokes and couldn't sleep.'

'I did sleep, but I am new.'

'I thought as much. Get yourself a mug and there's a pot of tea out there. Help yourself and bring the mug back.'

'Yes, Sergeant. Thank you.'

I went back into the kitchen, found a mug and poured myself a cup of tea. I also picked up a bread roll and put it in my pocket to eat later. Looking round the kitchen, there were other things that I needed. I found a salt cellar and a well-used tea towel that put in my great coat pocket. I finished the tea, washed the mug and put it back where I found it. I went back to the hut to retrieve my boots from the colander. They seemed softer, and I went back to the latrine block and washed the boots clean of urine. I then took them back to the hut while they were still wet and put them in the bottom of my locker.

It was still early, all the others in the hut were fast asleep. I looked at the brass buttons on my uniform and also the badges. They were dull. I needed to polish them. I had spent many hours sitting on the cabin top of *Ariadne* and later *Leo* polishing the brass rings around the chimney and all the brass knobs and brass oil lamps until they were gleaming. A Number One couldn't have dull brass work. Everything had to be polished bright every day. It appeared the army was no different – all the brass had to be polished bright. I only had the salt and tea towel, which I ripped into small rags and started to apply myself to the task. When I had finished, I put everything back in my locker and put on my uniform for the day. The wet boots I left in the locker.

Reveille sounded and the door burst open.

'Stand by your beds.'

It was the voice of our corporal. I complied and he was surprised to see me up, dressed and my bed made. He didn't know that it hadn't been slept in.

'Wakey-wakey, you miserable lot,' he said, as he started pulling the covers off the guys who were just waking up.

He came to me and stood facing up to me. I just looked directly ahead.

'You really think that you are clever, don't you.' He looked in the locker and found my boots that were dull and still wet.

'Put those boots on, and don't take them off for the rest of the day and tomorrow. I want to see them so that I can see my reflection in them.'

I turned round and put on my wet boots. It was really what I wanted. I needed to wear them in. They were now pliable and with them drying on my feet, they would be a perfect fit.

I had just finished putting my boots on when the hut door flew open and a sergeant came in. The corporal just froze and stood to attention.

'Now, who's this troublemaker I've been hearing so much about?'

The corporal said nothing. He had shot his mouth off in the bar and he was now being checked out. I stepped forward, saluted and said, 'I think that it's me.'

'Hmm.'

The sergeant went to my locker to see my uniform and great coat with buttons and badges gleaming.

The corporal found his voice. 'His boots are a disgrace.'

The sergeant looked down at my feet. 'You are right, Corporal. I will do an inspection tomorrow morning and expect to see an improvement.'

'Yes, Sir.'

The sergeant walked around to look at the other members in the hut, who were only partly dressed, and the uniforms were more or less as they had been collected from the stores. He turned round and left as quickly as he had arrived.

The door was no sooner closed than the corporal faced up to me again.

'You are trouble. You will wear those boots all day until lights out and I will be in here again at reveille to see them shining bright.'

'Yes, Corporal.'

He turned from me. 'As for the rest of you, you can get all your kit shining bright, including your boots, which are a disgrace.'

With that he turned and left us. The others in the hut finished getting dressed and we went to the mess for breakfast. It was true; the army marched on its stomach.

It was during the morning when the other lads were trying to clean their brass that I decided to have a walk around the camp perimeter fence. I was really looking for rabbit droppings or a feather off a pigeon or pheasant. What I did find were the signs of a couple of foxes, so there must be easy pickings around the camp.

I became aware of a jeep pulling up alongside me and two Red Caps got out to confront me.

'What are you doing?' one asked.

'Just checking the perimeter fence.'

'What about the fence?'

'I was wondering whether it was to keep me in or the IRA out.'

'What do you know about the IRA?'

'Wearing this uniform, they would take great delight in shooting me and just standing still, here, would make me and you a very easy target.'

They stopped looking at me and looked at the perimeter fence. Just beyond the fence was a slight rise that was covered in a small coppice, which would be ideal to conceal a would-be marksman. This wasn't missed by the Red Caps.

'Get in the jeep, soldier.'

I complied, and they drove quickly back to the guardhouse. They took me inside and put me in an interview room with a mug of tea. The sergeant was on the telephone to somebody. I could hear him almost shouting at whoever he was talking to. I finished the tea and stood up, waiting to be dismissed. He came in to see me.

'Am I free to go?' I asked.

'Yes, you can go. Just don't go walking around the perimeter fence.'

'No, Sergeant. Thank you for the tea.'

I left and wondered what that was all about. I might one day find out.

Back at the hut, new recruits had turned up and were making themselves at home, choosing the beds and lockers. In every group there is always one who exerted his male ego to become top man. There was one in this group, who saw my bed already made up and decided that it would be his. I didn't complain and just moved my things from my locker to the next one. I set about making the bed and had just about finished when the door flew open.

'Stand by your beds.' The corporal had arrived.

I just stood at the foot of my new bed. He came to see that I was still wearing my wet boots and then moved to my old bed. He stripped the bed, thinking that it was mine. The guy who had chosen that bed turned and started putting it back.

'What do you think you are doing?' the corporal asked.

'Making my bed.'

'Just don't move. How come it's your bed?'

I answered. 'Goldilocks couldn't decide which bed she wanted and chose that one.'

There were sniggers from the other guys in the hut.

'I'll get you yet,' he said, and turned back to see that the new recruit had not listened to the corporal's instructions not to move.

'What do you think you are doing?' he asked.

'Making my bed again.'

'I told you not to. You are on a charge. You can clean out the latrines for the next week and you can clean them with your toothbrush. Do you understand that?'

'Yes, Corporal.'

'What a bunch I've got. I will knock you all into shape, have no fear about that.'

He left us.

'Why did he strip my bed?' I was asked.

'He's picking on me. You didn't know that and have just found out. If I were you, I would not come anywhere near me, and that applies to all of you other guys as well. He always picks on one and this time it's me.'

It was grub time, and I made my own way to the mess for dinner. I returned to the hut to wait for lights out. I had found the boot polish that Paul was using and asked him if I could have the use of it. I would repay him when I had money to buy my own.

Before lights out, the corporal made another appearance, just to make sure that I was still wearing my boots. I was, of course, and he was both angry at me for not feeling any discomfort as well as for complying with his orders. He made a cursory inspection of the other lockers and gave each and every soldier the benefit of his tongue before leaving as the lights went out.

I sat down on the edge of the bed, waiting for my eyes to get used to the darkness. I went to the locker and collected my great coat and ordinary shoes. I exited through the window at the rear of the hut and went into the boiler room. I took off my boots and put them on the boiler to dry out, before I curled up for an early night.

I was awake at first light and found my way to the kitchen door to request another tea. The sergeant just waved his hand in acceptance of my request. Again, I pocketed a bread roll and also put the teaspoon in my pocket. I would need that to clean my boots.

I quickly finished the tea and went back to the boiler room to collect the boots. I thought of going back inside the hut, but decided to stay in the boiler room to clean and polish my boots. I needed the spoon to be hot so that I could apply the black shoe polish. I then polished them as vigorously as I could. It was a start, and after three applications of polish, they were coming bright. It was after another two applications that they were to my satisfaction.

It was while I was cleaning my boots that the boiler man came to stoke up the boiler with coke. He was surprised to see me. I told him that if he didn't mind, could I stay there? I would be no trouble and would keep his boiler room clean and tidy.

It didn't worry Bert any, and I think that he was grateful for the company. He had been a regular during the war and then stayed on as boiler man, and had been there ever since. He gave me a few tips on how to get the boots really shiny. I had made a friend who I could talk to and over the following days, he got my story out of me and how I grew up on the canal. I managed to 'borrow' a couple of mugs from the kitchen and we shared an early morning cup of tea as he gave me all the gossip going round the camp.

But that first morning meeting Bert, I was keen to get back into the hut before reveille, and I found the shower block. I went in and was amazed and pleasantly surprised by standing in what was like warm rain. I just loved it.

I returned to the hut, this time through the door as there was nobody about. I sat on the edge of the bed and went through my kit, giving everything a once over so that everything, including the boots, was as good as I could ever get them.

Reveille sounded and the hut door flew open. 'Stand by your beds.' The corporal had arrived.

He came straight to me, opened my locker and there were my boots bright and clean.

'Are these your boots?' he asked disbelievingly.

'Yes, I was wearing them all day yesterday.'

He was about to say something else when the sergeant came in. The corporal just stood to attention and saluted.

'Just checking that everything was in order.' He gave his excuse for being there.

The sergeant came over to me. 'Show me your boots.'

'Yes, Sir,' I said, as I went to my locker to show him.

'Hmm.'

'I was wearing them all day yesterday until lights out,' I explained.

The sergeant turned to the corporal. 'Is that correct?'

'Yes, Sir, I wanted him to break them in.'

The sergeant had seen enough and turned to me. 'Private, collect your things and come with me.'

'Yes, Sir.'

He then turned to look around the hut before addressing the corporal.

'Corporal Hunter, you will have your work cut out to even bring this motley crew to the standard that Private James has set. I have you in my sights. Leave Private James alone.'

He turned and marched out of the hut, with me walking behind him. We walked across the camp until we came to what looked like a garden shed.

'You can billet in here through your basic and then you will be posted. Keep your head down and be on parade in full kit tomorrow at

08.00 hours.'

'Yes, Sir. I'll be there.'

'Tell me, do you have anything to tell me about Corporal Hunter?'

'No, Sir, nothing.'

'That's good. That's the army way.'

The sergeant then turned and left me to sort out my new billet. It was nothing more than a garden shed. I made a bed for myself and hung up my clothes, and put socks and things into a box. I already felt happier.

The first day on parade was a disaster for me. Quick march, left, right, left, left. Left turn, about turn, right turn. I was OK with about turn, except all the others went one way and I went the other. I had no concept of left or right. On the canal, we only ever used inside and outside. The towpath was always the inside no matter which way you were travelling, and the outside was just on the other bank. After being shouted at all morning and all afternoon, next morning, very early, I went to seek out Bert. I asked him to tell me about left and right. He just laughed. He took his pipe out and sat down in the boiler house to explain to me that I had a left foot, left leg, left arm and hand. The other side of my body was right. It took me a long time to understand and react to the simple command, 'By the left, quick march.' Eventually I had it. Marching around the square later that morning, I kept up with all the other squaddies and the sergeant major shouted at other miscreants that were out of step or turned the wrong way. Marching and eating vast amounts of potatoes seemed to be what the army was all about. Many of the men had sore feet and blisters and were put on a charge, trying to be excused boots. My boots were like a pair of slippers, being pliable and moulded to my feet. I had no problem.

The second week was more or less the same as the first, except that this week we were given a forty-pound backpack and were marched around the perimeter fence. It only lasted about an hour, however all but three of us were totally exhausted or had blistered and sore feet. I noticed that the coppice on the small rise at the back of the camp had been cut down and cleared. I smiled to myself. So that was what had wound up the Red Cap, and he must have given the MoD the benefit of his tongue. I had lost the chance of catching a pheasant that roosted there. I needed to find where they had moved to, but all in good time.

It was the third week of marching that we were all given a Royal Enfield rifle to carry as well as the forty-pound pack. It seemed that they expected us to do everything with a rifle except fire the thing. We were all given an instruction card on how to put the gun together. It had no purpose for me, as I couldn't read what it said. I carefully examined the gun and worked out how to take it to pieces. I put the pieces down in the order that I removed them so that putting them back again was just reversing the process. I couldn't understand why everybody else kept looking at the instructions and taking a long time over the task. I realised that I would have to slow down to keep up with my group.

After marching around for a week in the early morning and afternoon, between times taking the gun to pieces and rebuilding it, they took us to the firing range. We had more instruction about loading a bullet and taking aim and firing. It was only then that they actually gave us one round, and only when we stepped up to the mark to fire. They didn't trust any of us to fire the gun in the right direction. I took my turn, took aim and fired. The recoil was more than I expected, and the shot veered off to the left. I needed to adjust the sights. My thoughts were totally on that. I needed a small screwdriver. My knife was too big and the point too small. I found a large four-inch nail and one lunchtime took it to the workshop where, using a grinding wheel, I made my little screwdriver. While in the workshop where my group were assembled for instruction, I found a small can of machine oil. It was just what I needed to lubricate and clean my gun.

That evening, I cleaned the gun so that all the dirt had been removed and then adjusted the sights, only to find next day that I had over-compensated and now the gun fired to the right. It was on my fourth attempt that I managed to get the gun to fire straight and hit the target. It was noted and commented on by the sergeant in charge of the firing.

'You, name and number.'

'Private James, 5693154, Sir,' I said, standing to attention and saluting.

'Tell me Private James, have you used a rifle before?'

'Yes, Sir, my dad had a .22 and taught me to shoot with that.'

'We've noticed that you don't follow the manual when you put the gun together.'

'If the enemy is coming at me, I won't have time to read the manual. I just put it together as I take it apart.'

'Quite right, soldier. Sometimes logic beats brains,' was his comment.

'I could put it together blindfold,' I admitted.

'Would you care to show me?'

I stepped forward to the table and slowly took the rifle to pieces, carefully

placing them in order. 'Permission to ask for three shells.'

'Granted. This I must see,' he said, as he gave me three rounds. I put them on the table.

I found my handkerchief and tied it so that it was a blindfold.

'When do you want me to start?'

'When you are ready.'

I fumbled until I found the stock and methodically assembled the gun. I then inserted the round into the chamber. Removing my blindfold, I took aim and scored a direct hit. I then put the second round in and fired that. The third round I fired it at the head of the outline and hit that. I shouldered the gun and returned to my place in the ranks.

I heard the sergeant say to the officer in charge, 'I've never seen that done before. He fired off three rounds within two minutes and hit the target every time.'

While the firing party was distracted I stole an unopened packet of shells and put them in my pack. There was no point in having a gun if you didn't have any bullets to fire.

I went back to standing in line. I was unsure whether the others in my group were impressed, envious or downright jealous of my skill. It had not been my intention to show off, but to check out for myself how quickly I could fire off several rounds. I was not concerned with what they thought.

Word must have got round the camp because while standing in line for dinner, Corporal Hunter pushed in to be next to me.

'Well, Mr Sharpshooter, showing off were we today?'

'Not at all, Corporal. I should advise you not to stand close to me on the firing range, as it has been known for guns to go off.'

'Are you threatening me?'

'No, Corporal. Have you ever seen what a round from an Enfield can do? It goes in large and comes out the other side with an even larger hole.'

'You are threatening me.'

'I'm just advising you to be careful around people with loaded guns.'

'I'm putting you on a charge for threatening me.'

He really was a bully and a coward. I would get my own back on Corporal Hunter. I needed to bide my time and take my opportunity when it arose.

I thought no more about it until the next day, when two Red Caps came and marched me to the HQ building. Inside, sitting at a large desk, was Lieutenant Colonel Bridge. Sitting alongside him was a captain, probably his adjutant. Standing to one side was Corporal Hunter. The Red Caps marched me to stand in front of the CO. I stood to attention and saluted.

'Name and number,' the CO demanded.

'Private James, 5693154.'

'Now, Private James, you have been charged with threatening a non-commissioned officer, what do you have to say about that?'

I just responded with my name and number. 'Private James, 5693154.'

'Yes, you have just told me that. Did you or did you not threaten to shoot Corporal Hunter?'

Again, I just responded with my name and number.

'Damn it, man. You have now told me that three times. I am your commanding officer and you will answer my questions.'

'With due respect, under interrogation all that I am required to give is my name and number, which is what I have given you.'

'Private James, you are in contempt of this court.'

Again, I replied with my name and number.

'Private James, answer my question,' he demanded.

'Under the Geneva Convention, under interrogation I am only required to give my name and rank. This is an interrogation and I have complied within my rights.'

'Damn you. I'm your commanding officer.'

'I think that the Geneva Convention commands a higher authority.'

The CO went puce with anger and turned to his adjutant. 'What can we do with him?'

'If we were the enemy, I'd send him back to where he came from. We are completely wasting our time questioning him.'

The CO sighed in defeat. 'I'm charging you with contempt. For the rest of your time here you will be working in the cookhouse and the rifle will be confiscated so that you won't have any desire to use it. Case dismissed.'

I saluted and was marched out of the HQ. The Red Caps took my rifle from me and I put on my fatigues and made my way to the cookhouse, where I presented myself for duty.

The sergeant looked up when he saw me. 'So, it's you. I was told. Go outside, where you will find bags of potatoes. Take a large pan and fill it with peeled potatoes, then get another pan and keep going until I tell you to stop.'

'Thank you, Sergeant.' I saluted and went out into the yard, collecting a large pan on my way.

I found an empty oil drum to use as a seat and started peeling the first of what would be a million potatoes. Working on the canal had given me a pace of life. Travelling along the sixteen-mile pound at three miles an hour was a five-hour trip. Nothing less, and sometimes more, but one couldn't hurry and it had a pace about the trip and the journey. I was happy peeling potatoes for as long as it took. I used my little knife and made light work of the task.

Sometime later, the sergeant came out to watch me and smoke a cigarette. When it was finished he dropped it on the floor and stepped on in. 'Finish up here and in there you will find a load of carrots. See how you get on with those. Oh, and get a mug of tea before you start.'

I finished up the last pan, took it into the kitchen and returned to the yard, to put all the potato peelings into the skip and wash the yard down. I then found a mug and had a drink of tea. I then went to see a mound of carrots. I brought in the oil drum to sit on and started on the carrots. I had no idea how long that took, but time was of no concern to me as I just paced myself with the task.

When I had finished, I cleared up and washed the floor down and went back to see the sergeant.

'What do I call you?' he asked.

'Jim.'

'Well, Jim, I don't know what trouble you're in to get sent down here but keep your nose clean, don't cause me any trouble and we'll get on fine. We eat first. Go and have a shower, change those fatigues and come back for an early dinner. After that, we will see how you get on washing up.'

'Thank you, Sergeant. Permission to leave?'

'Yes, and come straight back. We won't wait for you.'

I left, had a shower and returned to the kitchen, where I was given a plate of food. I looked around before taking out my knife to eat the meal. It was better than what was dished up to the squaddies. The cooks had the choice of the best. I had the task of scouring the pots as they were finished with and then the plates and dishes as they came back. I had no sooner cleared away one lot when an even larger number appeared. I pressed on. The cooks were no slouches. They scrubbed the kitchen down until everything was clean and tidy.

'Jim, that's it for today. You need to be here at four-thirty tomorrow morning to start breakfast. You will get afternoons off for a couple of hours. This is a seven-day-a-week job, so you won't be getting any leave any time soon.'

'No, Sergeant. How will I know what time four-thirty is?'

'Do you have an alarm clock or watch?'

'No, Sarge.'

'Just come at your normal time. You know what I'm telling you.'

'Yes, Sarge. Thank you.'

He sat back in his chair. 'Jim, you are the first squaddie that's ever been here on a charge that has thanked me.'

'I'm happy here. It's better than marching around going nowhere in particular for no reason either.'

'Away with you. See you in the morning.'

I saluted and left.

I was perplexed and annoyed that I had lost my rifle. It took me a few days to find out where the rifles were locked away. It was another Nissen hut with a well-padlocked door that seemed to be visible to the Red Caps. The next morning, in the early hours, I walked that way, going to the cookhouse not by the front door but round the back. There was a lean-to shed with a metal-framed window above. The window was one that could only be opened from the inside and I put my mind to how I could open it from the outside. I thought that painters would be able to open it from the outside without having to go around and open it from the inside. I jumped up on to the roof of the lean-to and looked through the rather dirty window. I could see the many, many racks of wire cages that had rifles piled up. The hut was full of guns. I wondered how I would be able to find mine, but I needed to get in first.

All day, as I peeled the potatoes, I gave the matter all my thoughts. It was probably like breaking into a car. I needed a long, thin piece of steel that would be flexible to be pushed through the gap around the openable window, yet strong enough to release the catch. No, it would be easier to break a pane of glass, remove all the glass and nobody would even notice.

I had to wait until the following morning, when I had my opportunity to try my hand at breaking and entering. Breaking the glass was easy, as one blow did the job. I carefully removed the glass from the frame and released the catch on the window and I was in. I collected all the broken shards of broken glass and took them with me to put in the cookhouse waste bin. It was left until later that night after lights out, when only the various bars were open and there was little or nothing happening around the base. I went via the shadows to the back of the store and quickly made my entrance. There seemed to be no end of bins with guns in them. It would take days to find my rifle, especially in the dark. I would have to visit again early in the morning when it was light.

For the next few days I spent a short time in the store. I would easily recognise my rifle. It was cleaner than all the rest and stood out. It was on my fourth visit that I eventually found my rifle and removed it from the store. I put the gun under the eaves of the lean-to and waited a few days to see if it had been missed. Everything was quiet, and one evening when it was pouring down with rain I took the rifle back to my hut, hiding it under my great coat. Once inside the hut, I cleaned and oiled the weapon. I took my knife and engraved my mark on the butt of the stock. It was a small heart. I had some shells but the sound of gunfire would be heard all over the camp, so I abandoned the idea of firing it.

The days passed, and I had a regular routine, when two entirely separate incidents occurred that would change my life. The first was one afternoon when I had free time away from the cookhouse. I was walking the perimeter fence furthest away from the prying eyes of the Red Caps.

What I was really doing was trying to find a spot to set a snare, hoping to get a rabbit, when I heard the sound of hooves pounding the ground. I stopped to see who or what was coming. It was a girl out riding, when the horse suddenly pulled up.

His abrupt stop threw the rider off. The horse was raising one of his forelegs. I went over to see what the problem was.

'Are you alright, Miss?' I asked, as I helped the girl to her feet.

'Yes, I think so. He's never done that before. Give me a leg up.'

I duly obliged and she swung her leg over the saddle. She tried to get the horse to move but he didn't budge. She slipped out of the saddle. I then recognised the girl. Damn, it was the CO's daughter. I disregarded her and stroked the horse's neck before standing in front of him.

'Easy, boy,' I said calmly, as I breathed out into his nostrils so that he could get a good smell of me. I stoked the blaze between his eyes and down to his nose.

'What do you think you are doing?' the girl asked angrily, and unsure as to what was happening.

'Are you alright, Miss?'

'Yes, but there's something wrong with Nobby,' she said, and started to cry.

'Stop crying. Horses are sensitive to upset. Smile and stroke him. Reassure him that everything's alright.'

'What does a squaddie know about horses?'

'More than I know about officers' daughters. He's lame,' I said, as I ran my hands over the upper part of the horses foreleg.

'There's nothing wrong with his leg, it must be his hoof.'

I put the horse's leg between mine and raised his hoof up, so that I could see what the matter was. There was a shard wedged under his shoe. It must have hit a sensitive spot and Nobby couldn't put his hoof down without being in intense pain. There was nothing for it but to dig it out. I released my knife and waited a few seconds.

'Take the halter and hold him steady. He is likely to jump.'

'Why? What are you doing?'

I ignored the questions. 'Just hold him firmly and don't let go.'

I went straight in and with one swift movement released the shard. The horse bucked, then put his leg down. I picked up the shard and put it in my handkerchief to give to her.

'This was the problem,' I explained.

'Where did that come from?' she asked.

'Wherever, doesn't matter. Nobby will have a sore hoof for a couple of days. Maybe you should get the vet out to see him, and also your farrier to check his shoes, but there won't be any more riding today.'

I found a carrot in my pocket. It was going to be my lunch. I broke it in half and gave it to the pony while I stroked his neck, giving him reassurance that there would be no more pain.

'I must be going,' I said.

'Walk with me, please. I'm sorry I said those awful things. I will get the vet round on Monday. I just hope that Nobby will be alright.'

'He will be fine. Look, Miss, I can't be seen talking to you otherwise I will be put on a charge, and I'm already on one, and you can't be seen to be talking to me.'

'I don't care. Just walk a short way with me. I'm Rachel, what's your name?'

'Jim, Jim James. They have put me in a shed to be away from the other squaddies as I'm seen to be a troublemaker.'

'Ah, so you are the troublemaker. Daddy said that he had a prize specimen with this intake. Sorry, I shouldn't have said that. Will you forgive me?'

'Nothing to forgive. Your Dad is entitled to his opinion.'

We walked along. Rachel had the reins of the horse in one hand and held my hand with the other.

'Jim, what were you doing so far from the barracks?'

I laughed. 'I was about to set a snare to try to catch a rabbit. I haven't had rabbit for a couple of weeks now.'

'What do you do, just catch them?'

'No, I skin them and roast them over a wood fire. It is one of the best meals that I know.'

'Would you catch a rabbit for me and cook it?'

'Sure, why not. Do you know that small stream on the far side of the base? Come around tomorrow any time after three, and if I can't catch you a rabbit, I might get lucky with a trout.'

'I know where you mean. I'll try to get away.'

'Rachel, I have to leave you here. We are too near the barracks and the Red Caps will be out after me.'

She held my hand firmly, turned and gave me a kiss. A real kiss, not a peck on the cheek but a real kiss on the lips. She then released me, and I turned and made as much distance between me and her as I possibly could.

I retraced my steps and found a gap under the fence, where I wriggled under and made my way to the small stream where I hoped to meet Rachel again the following day. I set my snare near a rabbit hole and just hoped. Being near the stream, I would have a choice of rabbit or a trout, if I could find a large one that I could tickle. So I had a choice and being satisfied with my work, I returned to the cookhouse the way that I had come. Nobody had missed me, and it was back to the usual routine.

The following day, after I had cleaned all the pans and dishes from lunch, I made my way to the stream. I found the snare with just a rabbit's paw hanging from it. I had caught a rabbit, but a fox had beaten me to it and taken the rabbit and left the snared paw. I removed it and set about making a fire. It would have to be grilled fish. I let the fire roar away and then smoulder with little or no smoke. I didn't want to attract unnecessary attention to what I was doing.

I removed my shoes and socks, rolled up my trousers and gingerly stepped into the cold, fast-moving stream. It was an ideal day, as the fish were rising to take the flies as they appeared on the surface. I slowly moved upstream until I found a trout that was only interested in his next meal. I put my hands under him and with one swift movement threw him on to the bank where I dispatched him, removed his head and gutted him. I then eased my thumbs along his bony spine to fillet it. I then spread it out on a frame made from twigs and a bit of string. I put the filleted fish alongside the smouldering embers to cook slowly by the heat of the fire. I threw the head and the rest of the fish back into the stream and sat down, drying my ankles and feet with my handkerchief before putting my socks and boots back on. I was hoping that Rachel would come by. The fish was cooked, and I was thinking that I would have to eat it all myself when Rachel came sauntering along.

'Hi, Jim, did you catch a rabbit?'

'Hello. No, well yes, I did, but Mr Fox beat me to it so I've caught a trout and it's ready to eat. I will just serve it up.'

I had found a couple of large dock leaves and some wild herbs. That was all that was needed, and we sat down on the grass to eat my meal.

'How did you catch the fish?' Rachel wondered where my fishing rod was.

'I waded in and tickled it and caught it with my hands.' Well, it was almost the truth.

'Wow. That's fantastic, and this tastes great.'

'It's living off the land. A meal is never far away. Tell me, how's Nobby?'

'He's fine, and I will be able to ride him next week or the week after. How do you know so much about horses?'

'I was riding Bill, our horse, from the age of two. He was a boat horse and pulled our boat up and down the canal. No horse, no money. We had to look after him and I helped Dad as soon as I was able. Sadly, Bill went to the knacker's yard and we then had a diesel engine. That's how I know all about horses.'

She smiled at my explanation.

We finished off the impromptu meal. I pulled up a clod of grass and put the fire embers in, then replaced the clod. I threw the sticks and dock leaves into the stream and nobody would ever know that I had been there.

I walked a little way with Rachel before heading back. We walked hand in hand. She was really nice, even if she was a posh bitch. She was a nice posh bitch. We parted with a hug and a kiss. I returned to the cookhouse and was unlikely to ever see Rachel again. But see her I did.

A week later I saw her riding Nobby again around the camp, so everything had turned out fine.

The second event happened over my last weekend on camp. I had been following the movements of Corporal Hunter, particularly in the evenings. He mainly stayed on the camp, going to the NCOs' bar after nine, when the lights had been switched off. He would stay until about eleven and then make his way back to his billet. On Saturdays, and occasionally on Tuesdays, he would go into the village. There was a late bus into Richmond that he caught, and returned on the last bus about eleven. He was drunk on Saturdays for sure, and maybe that would be my opportunity to confront my antagonist. What I was going to do I had no idea, but I knew that I needed to have my get even moment.

Time was running out for me. It was the Saturday before I was due to be posted on the Monday. All the squaddies had completed the basic and were fitter and slimmer from all the walking and parading around. The camp would be deserted, with just me and a couple of other recruits left.

The cookhouse sergeant asked me if I was going home. I had no home to go back to. I could look all weekend for my parents, and unless they were tied up at Bulls Bridge they could be anywhere between Birmingham, Coventry, Oxford and London. There was no way I could contact them; I couldn't write and they couldn't read. I explained this to the sergeant.

'Well, Jim, I don't need you here. It's going to be a quiet weekend. You can still come for your meals, but you can do your own thing and just chill out and hope that you get a good posting.'

'Thanks, Sarge. I'll just come round for my meals.'

The free time gave me the opportunity to pack all my things together. Most were sewn into the lining of my great coat. It became more than a little heavy but was easy to take with me, and with all the looking into my kit bag nothing untoward would be found.

Saturday night I slipped out of the camp, walking the far side of a vehicle leaving. I had my rifle with me, for no other reason than I liked having it with me. I walked to the village green to see if Corporal Hunter would go into Richmond on his usual routine. Having no squaddies, he might go earlier, and I was on the village green in the shadow of a large tree ready and waiting.

The first bus came and left. There was no sign of Hunter.

His usual bus came. All the late shoppers got off the bus and dispersed. There was still no sign of Hunter. The bus left without him. I had missed my opportunity to waylay him. I needed to return to the camp and made my way along the road, keeping as much in the shadow as possible. My walk was interrupted when I heard the muffled cry and scream. It sounded like a woman, and I went to a secluded spot in deep shadow where the cries were coming from.

I found Corporal Hunter sitting across the thighs of a girl. He had pushed her skirt up and was half lying on top of her, holding her by the wrists with one hand while undoing the belt of his trousers with the other. Getting closer, I realised that it was Rachel he was about to have sex with.

'What do you think you are doing?' I demanded when I was near enough to recognise both Hunter and Rachel.

'I'm giving this stuck-up little bitch what she deserves and needs,' was his reply, as my presence wasn't going to stop him carrying out his carnal desire.

'Rachel, do you want this?' I asked. She might be just enjoying this rough sex. I had no idea.

'No, get him off me,' was her plea.

I didn't hesitate. I just swung the butt of the rifle, catching Hunter on the point of his chin. It not only knocked him backwards off Rachel, but he was out cold.

I took Rachel's hand to get her to her feet and looked around. Hunter had chosen his location well, so that he could rape Rachel without attracting attention or being noticed.

'Are you OK?' I asked.

'Yes, just angry at my stupidity. I'd just arrived back on the bus from Richmond. He offered to carry one of my bags. What a fool I am.'

'Rachel, stay focused. Will you help me?'

'What do you want me to do?'

'Help me get him on my back and then carry my rifle.'

I lifted Hunter, and with the help of Rachel managed to get him on my shoulders.

'Where are you going to take him?' Rachel asked.

'The churchyard.'

We made our way across the village green to the small village church. Rachel opened the lich gate for me as I passed into the ancient graveyard. Not too far into the graveyard there was a newly dug grave surrounded by wreaths and flowers. I dropped Hunter and started moving the flowers off the grave. When the newly laid soil was bared, I used the butt of the rifle to make a small trench.

'Jim, he's coming round,' Rachel whispered, as she got my attention.

I swung the rifle again on to his chin and Hunter went back to an enforced sleep.

'Jim, what are you doing?'

'Burying him alive, well, only half covering him. Can you take his feet?'

Between us we lifted him into the trench I had made. I returned the soil, half covering him with it, then replaced all the wreaths around him.

'Rachel, after Monday, I won't be around, but he will be. How much to you want to get rid of him?'

'I hadn't thought about that. I don't want him anywhere near me.'

'Take your knickers off.'

'You must be joking. You're as bad as he is.'

'Rachel, when he comes round and he has your knickers with him he will not be able to defend your accusation that he tried to rape you.'

It raised a smile from Rachel as she wriggled out of her underwear and dropped them on top of Hunter. 'Let's get out of here.'

We walked back to the camp hand in hand, not speaking. Fifty yards from the main entrance I stopped and turned to Rachel.

'The last part of this is you running to the gatehouse, be out of breath and crying. You need to report that Hunter had tried to rape you and had just ripped off your knickers before you managed to get away. Have you got that?'

'Yes, Jim. I don't know how to thank you.'

'You don't have to. It was my get even moment. Now, run as fast as you can. You need to be out of breath.'

She put her face up to mine, and I put my free hand round her waist as we shared a warm and affectionate kiss before she wheeled away and ran the last fifty yards to the main gate.

I guessed that in the next fifteen minutes all hell would break loose, and I was in the wrong place with my Royal Enfield rifle, and if found I would spend more than a short time in the Glass House. I tossed the rifle over the boundary fence. I could collect that later. I then went to the main entrance, where I could see what was happening. There seemed to be Red Caps everywhere. I saw Rachel's father, the camp CO, come, and the MO. Rachel was going to be in for a hard time and I hoped that she could carry it off.

Suddenly, there was frantic activity outside the guardroom as the Red Caps were about to leave the camp in search of my old friend Corporal Hunter. I ran to the barrier and ran from one end to the other – on the wrong side. I was spotted.

'Eh, you, what do you think you are doing?'

'If you are looking for somebody, I'll help.'

'My God, some mother's do have 'em, and it looks like we have the prize village idiot. Get back this side of the barrier and get lost. This a police matter and we will deal with it.'

Rachel's father joined the group and witnessed this exchange, and recognised me. 'Get back in here and get lost. We don't want to see you again.'

I duly returned inside the base and walked slowly towards my billet. I would have to retrieve the rifle on Sunday evening, when all was quiet.

That wasn't the end of the affair. Sunday morning, I was apprehended by the Red Caps, who marched me off to the HQ building where an impromptu court had been set up. I was marched in before the CO and other high-ranking officers.

I stood to attention. Saluted and waited.

'Name and number.'

'Private James—'

That was as far as I got.

'Private James, this is not an interrogation so no more of that Geneva Convention crap.'

'No, Sir.'

'Corporal Hunter claims that it was you who was attempting to rape the young lady and he tried to stop you, but you hit him and knocked him out. The lady then ran away. What do you have to say about that?'

'Nothing, Sir. I was on the base all yesterday, as you remember, and never saw anybody, especially a lady.'

'Yes, you were being the prize idiot.'

'The other thing I would say is that I have never hit a member of the armed forces.'

'For once, I think that I believe you and that Corporal Hunter, thinking that you are that village idiot, could pin his actions on you. Private James, you are dismissed from this court.'

'Thank you, Sir.' I saluted, made a right turn and marched out into the Sunday morning May sunshine.

As I was leaving the court, I had my first chance of seeing Hunter. He was sitting between two Red Caps. His hair had gone white and his complexion was grey with black rings around two bloodshot eyes. I had given him the fright of his life. He would never be the same again. Now that was a result.

The news was all around the camp that Hunter had tried to rape

Rachel, and somebody had intervened and buried Hunter alive. He had denied the charge, but they found Rachel's knickers where he said he had been buried and nobody believed a word he said. The MO had intervened, as he said that Hunter was not in a mental state to be sentenced. He was discharged to a mental institution on Her Majesty's pleasure.

Sunday afternoon saw me collecting the last items together ready to put in my kit bag, awaiting further orders, when I heard a tentative knock on my door. That was strange. There was hardly anybody on the camp and nobody had ever visited me. I opened the door to see Rachel standing there.

I pulled her quickly inside. I didn't want anybody to see her.

'What are you doing here? If you are seen, I'll be in the Glass House with Hunter.'

'Nobody has seen me. They are all preoccupied with sorting Hunter out. I've just come to say thank you.'

'No thanks necessary. It gave me great pleasure and satisfaction to sort out a bully and a coward.'

She looked around what I considered my garden shed. 'Where do you sleep?' she asked.

I pulled out my bed, which was already made up. She sat on the side of the bed, still looking round. She took my hand to pull me to sit alongside her. I put my arm around her and we kissed. We really had a natural affection for each other, and we rolled back on to the bed, lying down alongside each other.

'Jim, did you get a supply from the MO?'

'Yes, but I don't know why.' I recalled that before the 48-hour leave, we had all been given cigarettes and contraceptives.

'Why don't we put them to good use?' Rachel whispered to me as she became more amorous.

Why not?

We undressed each other while lying down and spent all Sunday afternoon making love. At that moment I fell in love with Rachel, and I thought that it was mutual as she told me that she loved me. We were a modern-day Romeo and Juliet.

She sat up. 'Jim, I have to get back.'

I just nodded. I understood.

'Jim, when you get your posting, will you write to me?'

'Rachel, I can't read or write. I've never had any need to.'

She put her arms around my neck. 'Will you please learn to write and send me your first letter?'

There it was: I now had a real reason to learn to read and write, and rather than lose the girl that I had just fallen in love with, I would do that and write my first letter to her.

'Yes, I will learn to read and write and promise to send you my first letter.'

'Oh, Jim, I love you and thank you for everything.'

We kissed before getting out of my cot to get dressed. I looked out of the hut door, to make sure that there was nobody about, before letting Rachel go.

I didn't see Rachel again, but I needed to get that letter written.

Monday morning saw me in full kit, on parade, waiting my turn to be posted. I had to wait until I was called. I was almost the last one to be called. I presented myself with a salute, name and number.

'Private James; Wuppertal; cookhouse.'

I saluted. 'Thank you, Sir.'

'Where did you get that gun?' he asked. I was the only soldier on parade with a weapon.

'I was ordered to take it, clean it and practise putting it together. Nobody asked for it back.'

'Move along, next. Private Jones, Eric.'

I stood down and went to the cookhouse kitchen for the last time, to ask the sergeant what I was meant to do. He told me that there was a truck going to Wuppertal at 13.00 hours from the main gate, and that I needed to be on it.

It was my final activity and I had escaped with my rifle. It was another perfect result.

# CHAPTER THREE

*Army life and new beginnings*

I wondered what my new camp in Germany would be like. I soon found out.

The journey from Catterick to Wuppertal was long and tedious. The open truck was full as we huddled together in the back, with just a tarpaulin cover to protect us from the weather. The journey took the best part of 24 hours.

The camp was probably like all the other British camps in Germany and built to a pattern. We were settled in a Nissen hut and collected our bedding, and took the rest of our first day to get to know the base. I called in to see the sergeant in charge of the cookhouse. He was expecting me. He guessed that he had been given another useless troublemaker. I would be on duty first thing the following day. I guessed that it would be peeling potatoes, and it was. I found an oil drum and sat down, starting on the vast pile of potatoes. My little knife made easy work of the job, and I was used to pacing myself for many hours, walking behind the horse or polishing all the brasses as we travelled at three miles an hour for mile after mile. Sitting down, picking up one potato after another, was easy and strangely quite satisfying.

After I had made quite a dent in the large number of potatoes, the sergeant came to watch me as he smoked a cigarette. I paid no attention and continued at my same pace, without looking up. He dropped the end of his cigarette and put his foot on it.

'You can leave that for the time being. Come with me.'

I finished what I was doing and followed him into one of the cookhouse stores.

'There are at least five hundred chickens in there. Let's see how you get on preparing them for the oven. That's feathered, drawn and their heads and feet chopped off.'

The smell was something else. It was just a smell. I went and found a large pan of boiling water to immerse the first bird in and then quickly plucked it, chopped off its head and claws before drawing it. I put the entrails in a separate bowl and put the finished bird on to the tray provided. That was the first of five hundred, and I just worked steadily away. After doing a few, the sergeant came out to see me.

'I see that you seem to know what you are doing. How come you were sent here to the cookhouse?' he asked me.

'They thought I was a troublemaker.'

'What did you do?'

'Nothing, except try to do as I was told.'

'You do what I tell you and you will do alright. Step out of line, and I'll be down on you like a ton of bricks.'

'Yes, Sergeant.'

He turned and left me to get on with the job. It was a messy, smelly job. It was another test. Why did they always want to test me? I paid no attention and continued with the task until they were all done. I then cleaned up the room, putting the waste into the various waste bins and then hosing down the store and sweeping it out. Once finished, I went to see the sergeant.

'Finished?' he asked.

'Yes, Sarge.'

'Keep this up and you'll be fine. Go and wash and get changed and have a couple of hours off, and come back after lunch to do the clearing up.'

'Yes, Sarge. Thank you.'

He just sat back and looked at me before waving me away. I went and changed and had a shower, to get rid of the chicken smells. I put my fatigues in the general laundry with all the other kitchen overalls. They gave me a mug of tea as I watched the men come in for lunch. It was quite manic, but today they didn't want or need me to do the washing up. I was free until four o'clock, when I was wanted for vegetable preparation for the evening meal. That suited me, as I had a chance to look around the site. It was very much an operational base, with all sorts of comings and goings. There were parades, but there were more route marches and obstacle courses. They had mock-ups of houses that were used for training house-to-house combat. There was a constant sound of gunfire. None of that concerned me.

The days started to get into a routine. The work was nowhere near as intense as at Catterick, and I settled in with my new hut-mates, who always seemed to be exhausted. I didn't find any way that I could learn to read and write. I had nobody to ask. Again, I would have to wait for the opportunity to come my way, and it did in rather a strange way.

I had been there no more than a week when I was concerned about the collection of the kitchen waste. The stench was almost overwhelming in the heat of the day. I became aware of rat droppings around the yard each and every morning. We needed to get rid of the kitchen waste every day, and not let it hang around for days on end. I decided to try to do something about it. I went to see the sergeant.

I went into his office, stood to attention and saluted.

'Yes, what can I do for you?' he asked, as he sat back at his desk.

'Permission to speak?' I asked.

'Yes, what is it that you want?'

'Nothing for me, but it's the kitchen waste.'

'Not my problem. Contractors take it away as and when.'

'I think that it is likely to be our problem. We have rats.'

'Rats? I don't think so.'

'I've seen their droppings when I work in the yard in the morning. I think that we're infested.'

'Since you are complaining, do you have a solution that you would care to share with me?'

'Let me get rid of the waste each afternoon and then we can tackle the rats. If we try to just tackle the rats, we will never defeat them. They can breed every six-to-eight weeks and we would forever have a problem.'

'So how do you propose to dispose of the waste?'

'Don't know, but there must be a local tip around here and I could get a truck, and half the problem would be solved.'

'If you can get permission for a wagon, we will give it a try.'

'Thank you, Sarge. I'll give it a go tomorrow afternoon in my free time.'

I saluted and left. All I had to do was find a truck of some description. I went round to the motor pool and found what I thought was a wagon that had been well used and just left. I hoped that there was life in the battery as I hotwired the ignition, pressed the starter and at the second attempt it fired. I found the gears and drove it round to the back of the cookhouse. This would have to do.

After doing my morning chores, I put on my boots and set about shovelling out the bins on to the back of the wagon. It took longer than I expected, mainly because there was more waste than I had anticipated, but from here on I wouldn't let it mount up. When the wagon was loaded, I washed out the bins with strong disinfectant and then the yard. I put the shovel and broom on the back of the truck and drove over to the main gate, and was stopped by the security guard.

'Pass,' was his only request.

'I need to take this to the dump.'

'What have you got there?' he said, as he put his head over the side boards. 'My God!' He was overtaken by the smell and look of food waste.

'Do you fancy giving me a hand? I've got a spare shovel.'

'No chance. How long will you be away?'

'A couple of hours, with a bit of luck.'

'Just get that out of here and don't bring it back.'

'No, Sir. No chance.'

The barrier was lifted, and I was out and driving along the road on the wrong side, but I was free. I didn't have a licence, I had effectively stolen the truck, I had no pass, but I was free. I hadn't driven too far into the country when I stopped to ask a guy standing beside the road if there was a pig farm around.

'Eh, mate, is there a pig farm near here?'

He replied in German, which I didn't understand.

'Oink, oink. Farm, here.'

'*Ja, es gibt einen dar links,*' he said, pointing to a large building alongside the main road.

I thanked him and drove over to the farm that he had pointed out. As I drew up, I was confronted by a rather rotund man, who I thought was the farmer. He said something that I didn't understand but I guess he wanted an explanation.

I stepped out of the cab. 'Pig food. Oink, oink,' I said, and then pretended to put things in my mouth. 'Pig food,' I repeated.

'*Ein moment bitte,*' he said, as he went into the farmhouse and came out with a young lady dressed in the traditional dirdl. She came out smiling, wiping her hands on a towel.

'Do you speak English, Miss, because I don't speak German.'

'Yes, a little.'

'I'm a soldier off the base.'

'Yes, we can see that, but why are you here?'

'I work in the cookhouse. Each day I have kitchen waste, and you could have it as food for your pigs.'

'How much will it cost us?'

'Nothing. It's free. If you show me where I can unload it, I will make sure that there won't be any mess.'

She turned to the middle-aged man and he just nodded his understanding. I went back into the cab and drove to where he bade me. I reversed the wagon up a small ramp onto what looked like a pit. I shovelled the waste into the dump before finding a hose, to wash down the wagon and then the yard to sweep both clean. As I was returning to the wagon, the farmer took me by the arm.

'*Komm mit. Habst kaffee.*'

We sat down on a bench outside the farmhouse and his daughter came out with a coffee for me. I thought that this would never have happened in England. These Germans were friendly and hospitable.

'What's your name?' the girl asked.

'Jim, Jim James.'

'I'm Helga, and this is my father Herr Schwenkar. Thank you for bringing the food for the pigs.'

'It's my pleasure, Miss. There will be some more tomorrow and every day. Can I bring it here?'

'Of course. That's very kind of you. *Danke.*'

'What's "*Danke*"?' I asked.

'*Danke* is thank you. Don't you know any German?'

'No, would you teach me? I would like to learn.'

'Then that's it. I will teach you German in payment for the pig food that you bring. We can have two hours every afternoon. How does that sound?'

'Very good. Thank you.'

'*Sehr gut, danke.*'

'*Sehr gut, danke.*'

'There, you can already speak a few words.'

I felt pleased and thanked them again using the German words that I had learnt, and drove back to the base.

At the gate I was stopped by the guard, who looked on the back of the wagon.

'Where did you take that mess?' he asked.

'Somewhere it won't come back. Tomorrow you can come with me if you like, and give me a hand.'

'Get lost. Just take the wagon back to where you found it.'

'Yes, Sir.'

I drove the truck round the back of the kitchen, so that the waste could be dumped directly on to the back of the lorry without me having to shovel it out of the bins. The sergeant came out to see me and cast an approving eye over the cleanliness of the wagon.

'Where did you take the waste?' he asked.

'I found somewhere to dump it,' I simply replied.

'Having got rid of the waste, what can you do about the rats?'

'Do you want to help?'

'I need you to show me.'

I went into the cookhouse and found two carbon dioxide fire hydrants. I gave one to the sergeant and took the other myself. I also took a shovel full of grain and scattered it over the yard, and we settled down to wait. When everything was quiet, the rats started to come out of the drains and appeared more or less from nowhere, until the yard was full of squealing and fighting rats, each wanting to gorge on the grain. I had seen enough and knocked off the restrainer on the fire hydrant, and with the sergeant operating the other one we gassed the rats. When the last rat was dead and the fire hydrant empty, I found a wheelbarrow and started forking the rats to take them away.

'Where are you going to dump them?' the sergeant asked.

'We can throw them on the boiler and incinerate them.'

'Good idea…'

Before he could finish, we were confronted by the camp CO and a couple of Red Caps. 'What's going on here?' he demanded.

'Infestation of rats, Sir. We're on top of it.'

'My God, I wouldn't have believed it,' he said, as he saw hundreds of dead rats almost forming a carpet over the yard.

This was my opportunity. 'Sir, if I can remove the kitchen waste each and every day, we will manage to stay on top of the problem.'

'Permission granted. Just do it. My God. Carry on, Sergeant,' he said as he hurried away. I guessed that he didn't have the stomach for being a rat catcher.

I went back to shovelling the dead rats into the wheelbarrow.

'Jim, there's no need for you to do that. I will have a couple of squaddies on charges to work down here. Let them do it, and I bet that they won't ever want to come back here again in a hurry.'

'Sarge, I need to clear up the yard of all this grain. We can't wash it down the drains, as they will come up from there again. If we do this for the next few days until there are no rats left that we know about, only then can we stop. I think that you need to requisition more fire extinguishers.'

'I'll get that organised and let you clear up the yard. I think that you will fit in here, and I can see a stripe coming your way in the next few days.'

It was another result. Over the next few days we eliminated the rats and I had the OK to leave the base each and every day without a pass. The farmer unloaded the truck for me and I had a two-hour German lesson each and every day. I picked it up with ease, and Helga showed me how to read German. It was easy, as the phonetics never changed, and I was pleased and eager to learn. I hoped that I was a good student.

The days began to pace themselves out into a regular routine that suited me. I found a bike that had been discarded. It had a buckled front wheel and bent forks. In the workshops, the guys were pleased to show me how to straighten the forks and fix the wheel. I had a bike to ride around on. I was happy being in the army. I had a good job, the best of food, afternoons off the base, learning German, and I had a stripe. I was now a lance corporal and out of the privates' hut. Perfect.

I still had my rifle but had no opportunity to use it. I met Heinz, Herr Schwenkar's son. He told me that he was joining a hunting group that, once a year, went into the woods on an expedition. I offered to help him. I took him the Royal Enfield and showed him how to take it to pieces and clean it. It was too early to give him the case of shells. I tried to explain that he needed to gently put pressure on the trigger and not snatch at it. Also, if he was shooting a wild boar he needed to do everything quickly, as the boar would either run away or run at him. On the other hand, if it was a deer, the slightest sound would scare the animal off. After a couple of weeks, I took him the box of shells, and at the back of the farm we set up a firing range, where I taught him how to aim and shoot straight. He was delighted, as he had the makings of a being a good marksman.

One day, the sergeant called me in to his office.

'Jim, you can't read or write, can you?'

'No, Sarge, I don't know how I was called up.'

'You think that you are National Service.'

'Yes, I was sent my call up papers.'

'Jim, you were tricked. Did you sign a large piece of paper?'

'Yes, how did you know about that?'

'Just found out. You have signed on for five years, and you have another four years to go.'

This news shocked me into silence. I was angry and felt stupid and humiliated.

'Jim, you are the best lad I've ever had here. I gave you a stripe so that you could pull rank on the miscreants that ended up here. I will try to get you another posting, where you can learn a trade and when you get back into Civvy Street, you will be able to get a job.'

I was so angry that I didn't even thank him.

'Jim, I have watched you over the past year and you live by and with your knife. Just this once, will you show it to me?'

I shook my head.

'Please, Jim. I will let you have it back.'

I relented. I released the catch, and with one swift movement took it from its sheath and brought it down on his desk, through a few papers that were there. The sergeant sat back in surprise. I pulled the knife from his desk and offered it to him, handle first. It was the first and only time that I had offered it to anybody. The only previous occasion was my blood brother, Jonny Smith.

'Bloody hell! This is sharp,' was his comment as he scrutinised my handiwork.

'I keep it like that and shave with it each and every day.'

He gave it back to me.

'I suppose you made it.'

'Yes, I must have been about ten. I don't really know, as I can't count either.'

He shook his head. 'Jim, you need to learn to read, and also count. What have you done with your pay?'

'Nothing. I still have it all. Dad always had the money and while I've been here, I've eaten free and I haven't needed to buy anything.'

He shook his head. 'Jim, you are wasted here. It might take a few weeks, but I'll get you a better posting.'

I just turned and left in a bitter mood. It would never leave me, or so I thought.

# CHAPTER FOUR

*From a boy to a man*

It was about that time that Helga gave me a present. It was an English/ German dictionary. When she offered it to me I instinctively recoiled.

'What's the matter, Jim?' she asked in German.

I replied in German, *'I've never held a book in my hand before and never had one.'*

*'Oh, Jim, it won't hurt you. Look, let me show you what you do with it.'*

For the next two hours, Helga went through all the German words that I knew and could spell, as she had taught me to read and write at the same time, and then found the English equivalent. At last, this was my lead into reading and writing in English, but was it difficult? I thought that English was impossible. None of the words were spelt as they were pronounced. I could speak the language but not understand the words that went with it. I would need the German dictionary to help me. Eventually, I would see the English word, look it up in the German dictionary to get its meaning, and then recognise the word. It was a convoluted way of trying to read English, and even more difficult write it.

What was uppermost in my mind was writing a letter to Rachel. With the passing of time, I realised that although I considered that I was betrothed to Mary Lee, I had really fallen under the spell of Rachel who I had loved as a true lover, my own first true love. I needed to write that letter. I explained to Helga that I needed to write to Rachel and the circumstances arising from that. She encouraged me to put pen to paper. It took the best part of a week to compose and get the words down.

It was with trepidation that I took my letter round to Helga and handed it to her. I asked her to read it out loud to me.

Dear Rachel,

At last I have learnt to write and this is the
very first letter that I have ever written and
promised that it would be to you.

Ever since I met you I have loved you and
hope to see you again when I get back to
England.

Please write to me here in Germany.

Your best friend,

Jim

'Oh, Jim, that is a lovely letter. You must send it to her.'
  'Thank you for reading it to me. I didn't know whether it was correct.'
  'Jim, I don't know a girl that wouldn't want to have a letter like that.'
Back at the base, I went to the post and bought a stamp and
envelope. I didn't know how much they cost. I just gave them a note
and then they gave me some change, which I put back in the sock that I
kept in my spare pair of shoes. All my pay ended up there. I had no idea
how much there was, and I had no values regarding money. I had never
had any, and had little or no need of it.

I posted the letter and waited hopefully for a reply. A reply never
came, and I was posted away from Wuppertal to Hanover.

I managed to get a second stripe in rather a roundabout way. One
afternoon coming back from the pig farm, there was a traffic jam at the
main gate. I wound down the window and could hear shouting, in
German. Curiosity got the better of me and I went to see what the hold-
up was. It was one of the locals with a badly damaged bike. He was
angry, very angry, and was shouting at the Red Caps. They had no idea
what he was complaining about and until he was moved out of the way,
the base had come to a standstill.

'Can I help?' I asked.

'If you can get the geezer out of the way, we can all get on with our
jobs.'

I turned to the man and spoke to him in my best German. *'What's happened? Why are you shouting?'*

It was more than just shouting, he was giving us the full works of his swearing repertoire. I couldn't make head nor tail of what he was saying. I asked him to tell me quietly what had happened. Having spoken to him in German, he realised that I could possibly help him, and he told me his story that I related to the Red Caps. I was about to start when the CO arrived in his chauffeur-driven car, going out somewhere. He was furious that there was a hold-up to his schedule. He would have to wait like the rest of us. We all stood to attention and saluted.

'What's going on here?' he asked.

I explained that the man had been knocked off his bike by a passing car. The following vehicle was an army truck, which ran over his bike. He needed the bike to go to work. If he couldn't get there, he would lose his job.

The colonel turned to the Red Caps. 'You need to find the driver of that truck.'

'Yes, leave that to us.'

'Sir, may I say that the truck may not be one of ours but from another camp, and if that's the case we'll never find the driver. What I think we can do for this chap is buy him a new bike, and in the meantime, I will lend him mine.'

The colonel thought for a moment. 'Good idea, as long as you don't mind, and you trust him.'

'Yes, Sir. I think the MO needs to check him out. I think that he has cuts and bruises, and maybe more.'

The Red Cap sergeant came to my rescue. 'We will take him to the guardhouse and look after him.'

The CO went back to his car as the traffic jam was sorted out, and the old guy was taken into the guardhouse to be looked after.

I eventually drove in and returned with my old bike. In the guardhouse, the old man was being patched up. The MO confirmed that there was nothing serious, and man was pleased to have the use of my bike.

I thought that was the end of the matter, but like all things there was yet another twist to my story. I was summoned to the CO's office. I went straight from the cookhouse in my fatigues and duly presented myself. The CO was pacing up and down. He acknowledged my salute without looking at me.

'James, well done the other day with that German fellow.'

'Thank you, Sir.'

'How long have you been speaking German?'

'It's only what I've picked up from disposing of the kitchen waste.'

'Ah, yes, I remember you. You cleared out all those rats. Well, I have a problem that I would like you to help me with.'

I wondered what sort of problem, when the colonel continued. 'I think that it would be good PR if we invited that German fellow and his family for Sunday afternoon tea when we get his new bike. My problem is that I don't speak German.'

'Would you like me to volunteer my services in that direction?'

At last he turned round to look at me standing to attention. 'You would need to spruce yourself up and mind your manners, coming round to my house, but it really would get me out of a bit of a jam, if you can forgive the pun.'

I didn't know what a pun was, but confirmed that I would be in my best uniform. It was settled, and I returned to the cookhouse to tell the sergeant, who just burst out laughing.

Cometh the day, cometh the man, and I was present at the front door of the CO's house when the chauffeur-driven car turned up with the cyclist, his wife and family of a boy and girl. They were all in their Sunday best. I welcomed them to the base and showed them into the conservatory, where afternoon tea was laid out.

The colonel's wife was charming and came with their three children. I did the introductions before we sat down. The children had smatterings of German and English respectively and quickly made friends, seeing the funny side of mispronunciations and using the wrong word. I was the go-between, translating questions and answers.

The tea went well, with a couple of batmen in white tunics serving tea, sandwiches and cakes. It was all very English. I realised that this is what the bosses and privileged were like. It was a million miles from my humble beginnings. I had neither tea to drink nor any food during the tea, as I was really not part of that group.

There was a photo opportunity outside the house, where an Army Press photographer turned up for group photographs and one of me handing over the new bike. Transport delivered it to the house.

Afterwards, I went with the family on a ride around the base in the limo before being taken home. I rode my bike back to the base. Again, I had been off base without a pass, and this time it ended up with me getting another stripe.

I few days later I was called to the COs office, where he announced that fact. He also told me that he had been given a citation from the MoD in Whitehall for fostering good community relations and he was passing one on to me. So he took all the credit, and I had a piece of paper and a photograph in the local newspaper.

I had more or less forgotten about the incident when Helga announced that she and her boyfriend, Wolf, were getting engaged, and I was invited to the house party that coming Saturday evening. I really didn't want to go but Helga insisted, and so I went.

I requested a 24-hour pass and would stay at the farm overnight.

The sergeant asked where I was going. I explained that it was the farmer where I took the pig waste, and I felt unable to refuse his kind invitation.

'I wondered how you got rid of everything, and now I know. Well done you. What is this party?'

'I've no idea. I was wondering whether or not I should take some food with me.'

'Why not? Take a couple of bags of spuds and carrots and cabbage. I'll keep one of the ovens on and will show you how to make bread rolls. You could also take a couple of chickens.'

'Would I need to requisition them?' I asked.

'Don't talk bloody daft. Just take them. Nobody will ever be the wiser. The blokes in here have more fiddles and supply the local shops and eateries at Her Majesty's expense. You, Jim James, keep your nose clean and there is no chance I will ever check up on you. Now just go. I have a mountain of paperwork to get through.'

'Thanks, Sarge.'

And so, armed with vegetables and oven ready chickens, I turned up at the Schwenkars' farm in my best tunic with buttons shining bright. I had no civvies, just my army uniform.

Helga's mother, Mrs Schwenkar, was pleased with the food but frowned upon the British Army uniform. She took me into the house and upstairs to one of the bedrooms.

*'Jim, this is your room where you will sleep tonight. I need to find some of Heinz's old clothes that he has grown out of, for you to wear this evening.'*

I couldn't argue back. The bedroom was not large but had pine panelling and little painted scenes and designs on the panels. In a strange way, it felt like a larger version on my cabin on the *Leo*.

Mrs Schwenkar returned with trousers, shirt and waistcoat. She left me to get changed while she went back to the kitchen. I removed my uniform and hung it up. I put on the shirt, which had been handmade with lovely stitching. The trousers were like a thick woollen material, to be held up by highly decorated braces. The waistcoat was also decorated. I looked a real dandy. Dad had told me in the old days, Number Ones had clothes like these, and I was again back home as a Number One.

The dinner was not lavish but was sustainable, with schnitzel and sauerkraut and a chocolate cake with cherries and cream. I had never seen such a feast. It was just for the immediate families and me. I was truly honoured.

The table was cleared and friends of Helga, Wolf, close family and school friends came and were given drinks, of which the boys opted for beer. An Oompah Band from the local village came to provide music and I was cajoled into dancing polkas, mazurkas and waltz. It was Mrs Schwenkar who tried to teach me to waltz and I soon got the hang of it.

I gave dancing up and went into the kitchen for a glass of water. Returning to the orchard, where the party was being held with lights in the trees and music and laughter, I suddenly became homesick. We had never had a party. We never had good food and plenty of it. We never had nice clothes. Here I was, having a good time, while my mother and father and brother were dressed in rags, surviving from one meal to the next and working sixteen, eighteen hours a day. I put my glass of water down and went to my room and sat on the bed with my head in my hands.

How long I was in this state I have no idea, but my melancholy was interrupted by a knock on the door and Mrs Schwenkar came in to find me.

'Jim, what's the matter? We wondered what had happened to you.'
'I'm fine. I'm thinking of my family and missing them.'
'I'm sure you are.'

She came and sat next to me on the edge of the bed, and put her arm around my shoulders. I turned to her and openly wept on her shoulder. I couldn't remember ever crying before. That Miss Green in the school room at Brentford got close, but it was nothing like this. Mrs Schwenkar just held me until the moment passed.

I sat up and dried my eyes.

'Jim, we are you family now. You must call me Mama and Tomas, Papa. Heinz looks up to you and Helga dotes on you like a little brother. You are in the British Army and well on the way to becoming a man. You are in good health, and although you have no contact with your real parents, they are still well and I am sure that they are missing you. I want you to stand up on your own two feet to meet the world head on, and not be afraid of anything or anybody. Now, give your new mother a kiss, and I will let you go to bed and will see you in the morning.'

I kissed Mrs Schwenkar on the cheek. She got up and left me. I think at that moment I left childhood thoughts and actions behind, and took on the mantle of being a man. I was nineteen years old.

# CHAPTER FIVE

## *Another new beginning*

Not long after that, I had the news that I was likely to be relocated. I explained to Helga that, one day, I would just never come again. That was the army way and that's exactly what happened. The sergeant called me into his office one morning and handed me the transfer. I had to report to the motor pool in Hanover as soon as possible. I was told to pack everything up and be ready to move out at 08.00 hours the following morning. He would sort somebody out to take the waste to the Schwenkar farm. I didn't have a chance to say goodbye to Helga, Heinz or Herr Schwenkar. There had been a spin-off that I was vaguely unaware of at the time, but to converse with Helga in English, I had to speak slower and form my words correctly. I lost my distinctive canal accent.

That was it. No more cookhouse, and I was pleased to pack up my things and take the truck taking me halfway across Germany. With my two corporal stripes, I sat with the driver.

The journey to Hanover was slow, as the driver only seemed to manage fifty miles an hour on an autobahn were everybody else seemed to be going at twice our speed. Upon arriving at the base, I was shown my quarters and had the dubious pleasure of having a barrack full of privates to look after. That was my first task.

I went to the barrack and opened the door with some purpose, announcing my presence with: 'Stand by your beds.'

The occupants smartly stopped what they were doing and stood to attention, wondering what sort of bastard corporal they were getting.

I strode up and down the centre of the barrack, taking in the state of tidiness. Back at the door I turned to address them.

'My name is Corporal James. I don't want to be here as much as you don't want me to be. I will visit you as and when. I don't want you to cause me any problems, just keep the place and yourselves clean, smart and tidy and you won't hear from me. Step out of line and you will wish that you hadn't. Just enjoy army life and make the most of your opportunities while you are here.'

With that little speech, I left them to it.

Back in my room, I had a visitor. It was another corporal.

'Hi, my name's Pete. I've got the floor below you. How do you fancy going for a pint later?'

'Don't drink, sorry.'

'Where are you from?'

'Catterick and then Wuppertal.'

'What were you doing there?'

'Peeling spuds, mainly.'

'Were you at Catterick when they had that bother with one of the corporals?'

'Yeah, Hunter was his name.'

'Rumour has it that he was buried alive.'

'Yes, I had that pleasure. I don't think that he will ever get over the shock of waking up in a grave in a churchyard.'

Paul was speechless. 'I'll see you later then.'

I guessed he thought that I was either lying or had actually carried out the dastardly deed and was not to be meddled with, as I was probably a Jekyll and Hyde character to be avoided on dark nights. From that moment on the word must have travelled around the camp, as I was left alone, which suited me.

My first day on duty, I presented myself to Major Black, who was in charge of the motor pool. I was dressed in my fatigues ready to start work when I stood to attention and saluted. 'Corporal James, reporting for duty, Sir.'

'Corporal, eh. So who wanted to get rid of you so badly? It doesn't matter, you are here now. Just don't try anything clever, just do as you're told. Now, what do you know about vehicles and engines?'

'We had a two-cylinder National in our boat, and I can drive.'

'Well, that's something, I suppose. Do you have a driving licence?'

'No, Sir.'

'Right, you can start there. Go and see the trainer in Room G8, and tell him that I sent you and you need to pass your driving test.'

'Yes, Sir. Thank you.'

I saluted and left wondering where or what 'gee ate' was. I had to ask a passing private, who showed me the right door. I entered, stood to attention and saluted. 'Corporal James, reporting for duty.'

'Corporal, there is no need to salute me. I'm a civilian and this is just a day job for me. So, what did Major Black have to say to you?'

'He told me that I needed to get a driving licence.'

'Well, that's as good a place to start as any. Let's see what damage you can do driving round the camp.'

He led me out of his office to the small car park at the rear of the workshops.

'Have you driven before?' he asked, wondering where he had to start. Maybe he had to start with teaching me how to drive.

'Yes, every day in Wuppertal. It was a small lorry.'

'Every day?'

'Yes, I took kitchen waste to a pig farm.'

This answer seemed to puzzle him.

He pointed to a car. 'We'll take this one,' he said, as he handed me a set of keys.

I wondered what they were for. He sat in the passenger seat and I looked under the dashboard.

'What are you doing?' he asked.

'About to start the car.'

He realised that I was going to hotwire it.

'You don't need to do that. I've given you the ignition keys.'

I had by this time found the wires, twisted them together and then pressed the starter. The engine fired.

'Don't know what to do with keys. I've always started cars like this.'

'How long have you been doing this?'

'No idea. We've always done it. Is there anything wrong?'

'No, just try not to hit anything.'

I put the car in gear and set off around the camp. I didn't drive quickly and paid attention to the various junctions.

Back at the workshop car park, I pulled up in an empty space.

'Well, there's nothing wrong with your driving. I need to ask you about road signs.'

'English or German? I know both.'

'What does an English stop sign look like?'

'Can I borrow your notepad and I'll draw it for you.'

He raised his eyebrows, but nevertheless handed over his pad and pen and I drew the halt sign for him, including the letters. They didn't say 'STOP' as they did in Germany but something else.

He looked at the pad and took it off me.

'Tell me about traffic lights.'

'Red means stop. Green means go. The yellow just gives the warning that one or the other is changing.'

'If you are going at, say, thirty miles an hour, what's your braking distance.'

'How fast is thirty miles an hour?' I asked.

'A bit faster than you were driving this morning.'

'Oh, about from here to the front door, but I wouldn't be that close to the bloke in front. Leave well alone is my motto. I've no idea what he's doing, so I just keep back what I think is a safe braking distance.'

'Hmm. Have you read the Highway Code?'

'What's that?' I asked in my innocence.

'A book that explains how to behave and what to do when you drive around.'

'No. I've not read it.'

'Here, take this copy. Read it, learn it and I will ask you questions later and then you can have your licence.'

I thought that it would take me an age to find out the meaning of the English words, as I needed to look them up in the German book.

'Why don't you give me the licence now? I can go back to my billet and read the book there and you can check me out later.'

He just looked at me and my simple logic. 'I suppose it won't make any difference as to how you drive. I'll give you the licence, and you can give me the book back when you have learnt it.'

'Thank you. It might take a few days for me to learn everything, but I will give it back to you.'

It was only the second book that I had ever had. This was another result.

The following day I reported in at the workshops, where Major Black put me with a group of mechanics. Evidently, we worked in teams and did everything.

At one time, vehicles would have to be sent back to the UK to be repaired, but the army on the Rhine were stretched for cash, evidently, and had to do everything on the base. We would be kept busy, from just doing regular servicing to repairing crashed and broken-down vehicles of all sizes and shapes. It would be a good grounding for me.

I just loved the mechanics of the engines. I was never happier than when I was stripping down a diesel engine and rebuilding it. When the other guys in my group went for tea breaks and whatever, I would stay to sort out the various parts that were needed. The stores were in a complete mess and total disarray. I would spend my free time learning the codes of all the parts. I couldn't read but had to memorise the sequence of numbers and letters associated with the various parts. It was easy to me, and it was the start of me being able to locate the parts needed for whatever job we were undertaking.

I seemed to spend hours with the sergeant in charge of the stores, relocating the spares into some sort of order so that they could easily be found and vehicles quickly repaired. I think the sergeant thought that I was a real pain in the backside, but it made his job easier and he was praised by Major Black for the efficiency of the stores, with a minimum of waiting around for replacement parts on the shop floor. After a couple of years, he realised that it was my doing and I made my third stripe. I was then Sergeant James, who still had difficulty reading and writing in English and still couldn't count, but I could pull rank in the motor pool and stores for parts.

This all seemed irrelevant. I didn't want to be there and missed the freedom of being out and about every day. My only salvation was my bike. I could have a ride out and about. It had cost me twenty Woodbines to bribe the wagon driver to put the bike on the back of his truck when I was sent to Hanover. It was a small price to pay for my freedom.

The second or third weekend in Hanover, I discovered a canal while out and about. It wasn't a canal as I knew it but more like a cut bypassing a weir. I stopped to look. I had joined the ranks of gongoozlers just watching and looking. It was what the boaties called people on the bank that looked at the boats as if in a trance. The only difference was that I knew what was going on, and was enthralled at how the lock keeper kept the boat moving up or down but always forward.

The boats were not the narrow boats of the English canals but 200-ton vessels at least. They all carried their flags of country of origin. They travelled the length and breadth of Western Europe.

My observations were abruptly interrupted.

*'You can't stay here. You are trespassing.'*

It was the lock keeper talking to me in German.

I replied in German. *'I was just looking. I won't get in the way. Tell me, is there a boat yard near here?'*

*'Looking for a job, are you? There's no work around here on the boats or at a boat yard.'*

*'I don't want a job. I'm in the British Army, here in Hanover, and just like canal boats.'*

*'What's a German doing in the British Army?'* he asked. I was so fluent in German. It hid my English accent.

*'I am English, so is there a boat yard near here?'* I repeated my original question.

*'Hubert Maier has a yard on the far side of the river. Follow the river on your bike and you won't miss it. I still think that you are a German pretending to be English.'*

I left him to muse over that thought as I jumped on my bike to go in search of Maier's yard.

It wasn't difficult to find and I rode into the yard, which was like every other boat yard, full of bits of this and that with two lengths that had boats pulled up on them. I parked my bike and found the shed that doubled as an office. I knocked and walked in.

*'Good morning, I'm looking for Hubert Maier.'*

*'You've just found him. I'm Hubert Maier and what can I do for you?'*

*'I'm Jim James, I would like to work here.'*

*'Herr James, we have all the workers I need. There are no job vacancies here.'*

*'I don't want a job; I just want to work on the boats. I don't want payment. I'm in the British Army and just want to get out at weekends. I could come every weekend, Saturdays and Sundays.'*

*'What do you do in the Army and how come you speak German?'*

*'I've just started in the motor pool and I have had a good teacher regarding speaking German.'*

*'Come around on Saturday morning at seven-thirty and I'll find you something to do. We don't work Sundays unless it's an urgent rush job.'*

*'Thank you, Herr Maier. I'll be here next Saturday at seven-thirty.'*

I left the yard happier than I had been ever since arriving in Germany. I would learn all about German canals. Seeing the large barges trawling the length and breadth of Europe made me realise that back in England we were a hundred years behind, and unless things changed we would be overtaken by progress. What a predictive thought that turned out to be.

So, my stall was set out for what remained of my four years in the army, learning everything there was to know about the British vehicles, that were poorly made using inferior materials that had a propensity to break down at the most inconvenient time and place. When I received my third stripe, I sent the rookies out to recover the broken-down vehicles. It was a full-time job that seemingly never ended. We patched them up and sent them out again, only to see them a few days or weeks later. As soon as a vehicle came into the pool I knew what the problem was just by the sound they made. I realised much later that when you are deprived of one faculty, all the others seem to step in to compensate. Because I couldn't read, I looked and listened more acutely. I didn't know whether this was a blessing or a curse.

I could hardly wait for that first Saturday working at Maier's boat yard to come around. I put on my overalls and cycled out of the base at seven a.m. to arrive at the boat yard nice and early. I was first and had to wait for somebody to come to open up. Hubert Maier was a little surprised to see me and set me to work on blacking a boat. I would have called it painting, but I was given a large drum of what looked like bitumen and a mop to paint under the waterline, sides and bottom. The boat was about 200ft long. It was to be an all-day job. I just set to with the mop and when I had run out of paint from the first drum, I was given a second and then a third.

At lunchtime, Hubert called me into his hut and offered me a cup of coffee. It gave him an opportunity to quiz me about my origins and love of canals. I was a little reluctant to tell him anything, but as the days went into weeks, the weeks into months and then years, we became good friends and he drew my story out of me.

As my experience grew on the base in the motor pool, so did my experience on the boat yard. I was soon working on the boat engines and gearboxes. I was learning two trades, not one, but I didn't see it in that light. I was just as happy as I could be under circumstances beyond my control.

I had been at Maier's yard about a year when I found an old car under a tarpaulin in the corner of the yard. It was a lovely open tourer, the sort that Hitler and his ilk used to be paraded around in, saluting the lesser ranks and public in general. It was a 1930 something AU open tourer. It must have been there since the war, or even before the war. I asked Hubert about the car and had a short and abrupt reply.

'*It has nothing to do with me,*' was his only comment.

'*I was hoping that you would let me buy it so that I could do it up.*'

'*Take it, by all means. It is not mine to give you.*'

'*Whose is it then?*' I asked, wondering who would leave such a lovely machine to rot in a boat yard.

'*Jim, I tell what I know but don't tell anybody that I told you.*'

This was getting more intriguing. I wanted to know more. In fact, I wanted to know everything.

'*Towards the end of the war, one of Hitler's generals decided the Western Front was a safer option than the East. He came over here and jumped on a Swiss boat heading towards Basel. The boat got caught in the crossfire and sank, taking General Adler to a watery grave. His driver surrendered even before the firing started. I've no idea what happened to him, but the car was left here. So if you want it, just take it and don't involve me.*'

'*Thanks, Hubert. I need to get it moving to work on it at the base. So, could I come here on Sundays? I wouldn't touch anything but just work on the car.*'

'*If it gets it out of my yard, take it, and I'll give you a key for the yard gates.*'

And that's how I managed to get a monster classic car from yesteryear. I now had a Sunday project. Over the three years I effectively rebuilt it. I thought of taking it back to the base but too many questions might be asked, and there was also the possibility of revenge or just good old-fashioned envy coming into play that would damage or destroy what was now fast becoming my car. Hubert didn't seem to mind that it was still on his yard, and after the first few weeks nobody was interested in looking under the cover.

I had the opportunity of taking some items back to the base to work on in the evenings, while everybody was in the bar drinking or taking up some sort of sport. The men coming into the motor pool were not interested in anything other than drinking and trying to get the barmaids' knickers off. I considered that I was still betrothed to Mary Lee, but had this feeling of being in love with Rachel. I had never heard from either of them all the time I was in Germany.

The squaddies, as I still referred to them, were constantly leaving their tools where they dropped them. I was forever picking them up and putting them away, until I had the idea that they would be permanently 'lost' and had the squaddie put on a charge and his pay docked to buy a replacement. Over the three years of restoring the AU, I managed to accumulate a comprehensive and complete set of tools. I just thought that it was all part and parcel of one of the many army fiddles that everybody seemed to want to get involved with. I gave it little or no thought.

It was after a couple of years being on the boat yard that a boat came in for urgent repairs. They had been rammed in the stern and had damaged the rudder and steering mechanism. The yard dropped all other work to remove the helm and reconstruct it. The guys on the boat had an enforced holiday without pay.

I joined in the work at the weekend and we all had meals together that the crew provided. There were three hands to a boat so that it could work around the clock, night and day. They were interested in the English canals and about me growing up as a canal kid. I had made three good canal buddies. It was Sunday evening when the boat was relaunched, and we all had a drink of schnapps, when they asked if I had any leave due. I had never taken any so there must be. They invited me to come with them for a couple of weeks, so that they could work four-handed. Wow, what luck. What an opportunity. I gladly accepted, and they gave me their itinerary so that I could join them in a week or so. It would give me time to put in my leave request.

And so it came to pass a couple of weeks later that I cycled to the railway station and caught the train to Koblenz, taking my bike with me. I found them tied up at the wharf and was welcomed aboard, where they installed me in a fore end cabin. There wasn't much headroom but there was a stove and a bunk, and that's all I needed. The saloon, galley and other accommodation were in the rear above the engine room. It was a great couple of weeks. We went along the Mosel to Cochem before retracing our journey and travelled the Rhine, and then across country, ending up in Hamburg on the Elbe. It was the end of my two weeks. I had taken my turn on the long straight runs of canal, giving the other guys a well-earned rest from travelling all day and all night. I also helped out in the galley. I had picked up more than a few cooking tips in the cookhouse at Wuppertal and put them to good use. We all ate well and worked as a team. What I was about to find out was that they played out as a team as well.

'*Jim, this is your last night on board and we are in Hamburg,*' Kurt, the captain gave his little speech.

'*Yes, I've had a great time and can't thank you enough.*'

'*You don't have to thank me. When you leave the army come and join me and the rest of the crew. We could have a great time and we might see our wages drop a little, but it would be worth it, having you on board.*'

'*Kurt, I've told you, I don't want payment, and thank you for your kind offer but I really miss my family and my own boats.*'

'*Well, at least let me pay for your rail ticket back to Hanover.*'

'*Thanks, I would appreciate that.*'

'*So, are you coming with us tonight?*'

'*Where to? I don't drink and go round the bars.*'

Kurt laughed. '*Jim, this is Hamburg. We can't not visit the ladies of the Reeperbahn.*'

'*What does that mean?*' I asked in my innocence.

'*Don't you like women?*'

'*Don't know any. All I see are blokes at the base.*'

'*I can see that we will have to finish off your education.*'

'*Kurt, I don't want to seem ungrateful, but I would just rather stay here on the boat if you don't mind.*'

'*That's fine, Jim. I don't want to put you in a difficult situation. Now, I need to have a shower and get changed, ready for going out.*'

I went into the galley and cleared up the dinner things, putting everything away. They went out and I went to my cabin to pack what few things I had brought with me, and fell asleep.

I was awoken by the men coming back, and there were laughs coming from what sounded like women. I got up and went to the saloon to see what was going on.

They had returned with bottles of beer and schnapps and four ladies of the night. They were all laughing and drinking and getting into a state of undress.

'*Ah, Jim, there you are,*' Kurt said, greeting me with a flourish of his hand that held a bottle of beer as he had his arm around a well-endowed lady. '*Come and have a drink. We have brought a lady for you. You can choose any one, as it doesn't matter as we will have all of them.*'

I realised that he had found the ladies on the Reeperbahn and they were in for a good time. I really wasn't interested.

'Thanks, Kurt. I'll just turn in if you don't mind.'

'If you don't want to choose one, we will ask the ladies if one of them wants a virgin for the night.'

I was going to protest, but I while I was searching for the right words one of the girls just said, 'I'll see to the little virgin,' and came and took me by the hand. 'Where's your cabin?' she asked.

I was going to protest but she just smiled at me. It was a reassuring smile. She couldn't be more than twenty years old, and already in the world's oldest profession. I took her over the deck to my little fore end cabin, where we sat down on the bed and she started to get undressed.

I just sat down and watched.

'Tell me that you really aren't a virgin, are you?'

I shook my head. 'No. I'm betrothed to my childhood sweetheart and fell in love with another girl before being sent here by the army.'

She leaned across to me. 'I wish that I had a boyfriend like you. Not interested in other girls but just me.'

'Look, I don't know what to call you, but I've never paid for sex and have no intention of starting with you.'

She just turned round to me and smiled. She was now down to her underwear. 'My real name is Anna. Lulu is just a business name. Kurt has already paid me. So, Jim, make love to me as if I was your girlfriend and not a whore, and just for tonight I will have a boyfriend who loves me for who I am and not what I am.'

I took her in my arms and kissed her. It was the start of a night of lovemaking where I pretended that she was Rachel and I was her make-believe lover.

I was hardly asleep with a million thoughts running through my head and not one making any sense. I got up out of my bunk and got dressed. I went to sit on the cabin roof. The night was dark and still, with just the reflection of the city lights on a dead calm stretch of water. This was what I missed most of all. I just sat still, taking everything in. I heard a disturbance in the cabin and Anna came to see where I had disappeared to.

'What are you doing out here?' she asked.

'Get a blanket and come and sit with me,' I asked.

She returned with a blanket. I sat her on my lap and wrapped the blanket around her as she rested her head on my shoulder.

The silence was broken by the call of heron, as the dark blue of the night sky became light blue almost white as dawn was breaking. Slowly the sun rose, turning everything into a golden hue, and the various shades of red as the light picked up the clouds that was reflected in the water. It was a magical moment that I shared with Anna and wished that it was Mary.

But it wasn't. The noise of the wakening city impinged on our solitude, so I took Anna back into the cabin. She was chilled, and I warmed her as we embraced, falling back to sleep. She was a lovely young woman and I wondered how she had come to be a prostitute. As likely as not, I would never find out and I would never ask.

This falling in and out of sleep was shattered when there was a loud hammering on the cabin roof. *'Wakey-wakey, you two lovebirds. Room service is here with coffee.'*

It was Kurt's laughter, which faded. I went out to find two cups of hot coffee. I went back to bed and sat up with Anna to drink it.

*'I have to go back to camp today.'*

*'Do you have to? You could stay with me.'*

*'If I don't, the Military Police would come looking for me and I would spend time in jail. I need to get up, dressed and go.'*

She gave me her card, on which she wrote her home telephone number. *'Jim, please call me and come to stay with me.'*

*'Thanks, I might just do that.'*

I left Anna, found my bike, said my goodbye to Kurt and rode to the station to catch my train back to the base in Hanover. Back at the base, I found Anna's card and pinned it up on the back of the door, to remind me not to fall in love with a whore. I never called Anna and never saw her again.

# CHAPTER SIX

*The return of the reluctant prodigal*

My days at Hanover were numbered and the number was getting fewer as each day passed. The car was finished, except for the upholstery. It was now painted bright red. It was the only colour that I could find on the base that wasn't either matt green or brown. It was Post Office red. I loaded all the tools into the boot area, ready for driving back to England. I would have to come back for that. I had already explained that to Hubert. He was now concerned that I was leaving, and he said that there was always a job waiting for me working for him. It was an offer that I wouldn't take. I was homesick. He could see that, and I was more like a son to him than he cared to admit.

I knew my time in Hanover was getting shorter when I was called in to see Major Black. He was sitting at his desk, surrounded by papers.

'Jim, come on in. I've the papers here for you to sign. I would like you to sign on for another seven years, and to stay here running a section of the motor pool. I would promote you to be a second lieutenant with a spot of admin training.'

I was repelled. I wasn't going to sign anything – ever! 'Thank you for giving me the opportunity. I would need to think it over,' I responded in a non-committal way.

'Think it over, by all means. Take the form with you and drop it in anytime over the next few days or so.'

I took the form. Stood to attention, saluted and left his office. I threw the form in the first bin that I passed. I had been caught once. It would never happen a second time.

That wasn't the end of the matter. He called me in to see him again a week later.

'Ah, Jim, come in. Do you have the form for me?'

'No, Sir, I've no intention of staying in the army.'

'Ah, that's a pity. You could do well for yourself here. You would be out by the time you were thirty, and have management skills to go back into Civvy Street and with a healthy pension to boot. I would think that within the seven seven years you would rise through the ranks, and I see you as a possible replacement for me as I take another promotion.'

Major Black was a career soldier, which I would never be.

'Major Black, I was tricked into signing on. I have had no contact with my family for five years now and need to go home.'

'Yes, you can take an extended leave, but this is too good an opportunity to miss. When you go home, you will have no job to go to, and the way the unemployment figures are at the moment you are unlikely to get a job, so why not sign to come back here to continue your career.'

'I need to go home and pick up my life again.'

'Your life is here, in the army. We will look after you and you need worry no more.'

He wasn't listening to me. I was wasting my breath.

'Thank you, Sir. I will give it more consideration.'

'That's the spirit. I think that you will make the right choice.'

I did. I didn't sign on again and Major Black didn't push me further, until I was advised that I needed to report back to Catterick to get discharged. Major Black had given up on me and left me to my own fate, which pleased me.

I collected my things together, saying goodbye to Hubert Maier and promising to come to see him as soon as I could. I left my bike to whoever wanted it.

The journey back to England was better than coming over. I could sit in the cab with the driver; it was marginally more comfortable and definitely warmer.

Back at Catterick, I just had one night in the sergeants' quarters. I asked about Rachel and Lieutenant Colonel Bridge. He had retired, and nobody knew anything other than he was no longer in charge and there was a new man at the helm. I had no desire to see him or any of the officers.

The following day I went to the quartermaster's store, where I gave my name and the colonel in charge fitted me out with a demob suit that fitted where it touched. He also put a brown paper parcel tied up with string on the counter. He had a piece of paper in his hand that he put down alongside the parcel. He handed me a pen.

'Just sign on the dotted line,' he instructed me.

I had been down this route before.

'What am I signing?' I asked.

'It's just to say that you have collected the items you came in the service with.'

'I'm not signing anything. You can throw those things in the bin and you can wipe your arse with the form.'

'Are you being insolent?'

'Yes! What are you going to do about it? Come hell and high water, I shall be out of the front gates tomorrow, and neither you nor the rest of the Queen's army will stop me.'

I just turned and left him to look after his precious stores.

I didn't just escape as easily as that. I had to visit the MO to get a full bill of health and several packets of contraceptives. When I would ever get round to using those, I had no idea. I was also given two hundred Woodbines as they were deemed to be good for me. That was another waste, but it filled my suitcase that was also provided for me.

I recall leaving the barracks and retracing the steps I had taken five years before, going to the railway station and catching the train to King's Cross.

It was afternoon by the time I found myself on the canal at Camden Lock. It was strangely quiet, with no boats moving. There were a couple tied up and I went over to them. There was a youngish man sitting on the cabin top, smoking a cigarette.

'Eh, mate, have you seen the *Leo*?' I asked.

'The last time I saw *Leo* it was half sunk at Rickmansworth.'

'What happened to the Jameses?'

'Who are they? Never heard of them.'

I realised that things had changed, and not for the better. If I could get to Bulls Bridge, Mr Mostrop would know. I had the problem of getting there. I then wished that I still had my bike. This bloke had a bike on his cabin roof.

'Eh, mate, I'll give you ten bob for your bike.'

'Ten bob? Don't make me laugh,' he replied with feigned disgust.

'Ten bob's ten bob.'

'A quid would be better.'

'If I had a quid I'd offer you a quid.'

He looked at me in my demob suit and recognised the signs. 'How long have you been demobbed?'

'First day. Look, I've only got ten bob, so how about ten bob and twenty Woodbines?'

He thought for a moment, realising that it was the one and only offer that he was ever likely to get. 'OK, then.'

I fished out a ten-shilling note and handed that to him, and then found a packet of twenty Woodbines to complete the transaction. I took the bike off him and set off, riding the twenty miles to Bulls Bridge.

The canal was quiet. It was dead. During my absence something had happened. There were boats, but they were all tied up and devoid of people. At Bulls Bridge there were still boats tied up but there was only smoke coming from three or four. The rest were empty. It was all very strange to me. It was as if the place had become a boat graveyard.

I parked my bike outside Mr Mostrop's office, knocked and walked in. Mr Mostrop was standing looking at some papers. When I walked in he looked over his reading glasses to see who his visitor was.

'Well I'm blowed, if it isn't Jim James. What happened to you? You just vanished off the face of the earth.'

'Hello, Mr Mostrop. I was tricked into signing on for five years and have only just got out of the army.'

'Well, it doesn't seem to have done you any harm.'

'Health maybe, but my temper is raw from the experience. What's happened here? Where are Mom and Dad and the boats?'

'Ah, I remember you couldn't read or write, and neither could they. Trade dropped during the hard winters and everything went by road. The government also made the children go to school, so there was no more living on the boats. Your boats were tied up at Rickmansworth and your folks went to live on the bank. I have their address here somewhere.'

So that was what had happened.

Mr Mostrop went to his filing cupboard and had a card that he copied out on to a piece of paper.

'Did the army teach you to read?' he asked.

I shook my head. It hadn't been the army, it had been Helga

teaching me German.

'Well, go up to Ricky and ask there. Somebody will tell you. How did you get here anyway?'

'On a bike.'

'You won't get to Rickmansworth on a bike tonight. I'll tell you what; kip down in the end butty for tonight and I'll turn a blind eye. The chip shop is still open, and you can get a meal there tonight, but you need to be on your way first thing tomorrow.'

'Thank you, Mr Mostrop,' I said, as I took the piece of paper and made my way to the end butty and climbed on board. It was dusty, but it was a roof over my head. I searched round for something to burn and soon had a fire going in the old range. It would dry out the cabin.

I made my way to the chip shop and had fish and chips served in paper, and ate them with my fingers. They tasted awful. Army food was filling and basically good. This was stale and greasy. It was warm and that's all.

Despite the sparseness of the butty cabin, it felt that I was at last approaching home. I was up early and away on my bike. There were only a few boats moving and the towpath was in an awful state. Too many boats going too quickly, washing the banks into the canal. I was glad that Mr Mostrop had given me the use of the butty. Riding my bike along the towpath at night there would have been every chance that I would have ended up in the canal.

I arrived at the locks in Rickmansworth and further along the length on the opposite bank were *Leo* and *Ariadne*, tied up and half sunk. They looked to be in a bad way. I couldn't understand how Dad could let them get like that.

Returning to the main road, I asked a postman where my parents lived, showing him the address Mr Mostrop had given me. He gave me directions. It was in a street of terraced houses built in the middle of the nineteenth century. They were just two up and two down. I parked my bike outside number 37 and knocked in fear and trepidation. My stomach was churning with apprehension. I had wanted this moment for so long, and now that it was with me I wanted the earth to open and swallow me up. What sort of reception would I get? I soon found out.

My second persistent knock saw the door open and a little old lady tentatively crack the door to see who was calling. Then she threw it wide open and I had my mother in my arms, as she sobbed onto my shoulder. Words were not needed.

I heard a voice from inside demanding, 'Who is it, Else?'

Mom turned from me. 'It's Jim. He's come home,' was her simple reply.

'Jim? Jim! Where the hell have you been?'

'Now Dad, you can stop that. He's here and home at last. Don't ever go away again, Jim. You can't believe how we've all missed you.'

'And I've missed you and the canal and everything.'

I was led into the back kitchen, where I was made a cup of tea and sat down to tell them of my escapades, well, a few that were worth telling.

A young girl came in with a small child on her hip.

'This is Annie, Bobby's wife, and the baby is Poppy. She's coming up to two.' Mom filled in the detail.

'Hi, Annie, I'm Bobby's big brother, Jim.'

'I've heard nothing but "Jim this" and "Jim that" ever since I've been here. Are you staying long or are you just calling in?'

It was the question that everybody needed to know the answer to, but it had been left to Annie to ask the question. She was slightly built with large out-of-proportion breasts and with Poppy on one hip; she used the other hand to smoke her cigarette. Her dress was thin and hung on her slender frame. I wondered why Bobby had chosen Annie as a life partner.

'Where's Bobby?' I asked.

'When we were forced off the canal by this excuse for a government, he had to go to school, and now he is a stoker on the railway. It's early mornings. He will be back about four this afternoon.'

It was later that Mom told me that Annie had lived up Birmingham way, and Bobby had got her pregnant and they had to get married. I wondered about that. Maybe Bobby was a softer option than her other suitors who just had their way with her, and didn't want the millstone around their necks that would be a bundle of joy called Poppy. I let that thought remain a thought and didn't verbalise it.

'Jim, where are you staying?' It was Mom asking the question.

'I spent last night on an abandoned butty at Bulls Bridge. I have come straight here from being discharged from the army.'

'We are overcrowded here but until you can find something, you are welcome to spend the night in the front room.'

'Thanks, Mom. I might just have to do that.'

I realised that Annie was looking me over, for what reason I had no idea, but I soon found out.

'Jim, do you have any money?' she asked.

'No, I don't have a job either. I was hoping that I could work the boats with Bobby.'

'Jim, the cut's dead.' Dad made his assessed contribution.

I looked at him. He was an old man way before his time. He couldn't read or write; he couldn't drive; he had never done anything other than work on the canal. There was no job for him, no money other than off the dole and social. He had lost all his dignity and was a broken man. It grieved me to see him like this, but there was little or nothing I could do to help. I would try to break him out of that frame of mind. It had dragged him down as well as everybody else.

I got up. 'Where's your coat, Dad?' I asked.

'Where are you going? You've only just got here.'

'To get our boats back. I have free lodging, all that I have to do is get them back floating and you will know where I am and what I'm doing.'

'What now?'

'What else are you doing that's more important? Get your hat and coat.'

He went and put his old coat on and his battered trilby. He gave me an envelope.

'This came. I can't read it, but was told that it was notice to move the boats or have them taken away.'

I looked at the letter. I could read enough to see that it was from the British Transport Commission. We needed to go without delay.

Walking with Dad back to the canal gave me time to catch up with what had happened during my absence. Everybody expected me back and wondered and worried at my disappearance. Bobby was called up and rejected and came straight back again. It had been hard work with just Bobby and Dad getting frail, with more work falling on Mom. Work had almost ceased on the canal and families had all dispersed. What trade that was left was run by young, single men, which is how it all started in the first place.

Back at the canal, the boats were still exactly as I had previously seen them. They were on the far bank and I used a flattie maintenance boat that had been moored on the towpath to ferry me and Dad across the canal to have a closer look at the boats. They were both full of water. I was hoping that it was rainwater and not a leak.

The engine room of *Leo* was half full of water. I reached inside to find the manual bilge pump. I decided on doing *Ariadne* first. The manual pump was a simple device which was mainly a pipe and a plunger on a long pole. It was heavy work and I realised that it was beyond my father's strength. I pumped slowly and methodically, not tiring myself out after a few lifts of the plunger. It really was slow work, but after a couple of hours the boat was as good as empty of water. As soon as the back cabin had been cleared of water, Dad lit the stove to get some heat into the cabin.

We stopped for some lunch. It was a bag of chips from the local chip shop. Dad bought the chips with what little money he had. I still hadn't touched mine. I would see how things turned out.

The afternoon was spent pumping out the engine room of *Leo*. Once the engine room was clear, I made sure that the engine worked. I primed the fuel pump by hand and checked the injectors. Now this was hard work, as I manually turned over the flywheel and Dad threw the lever to drop the exhaust valve to get compression and hope that the engine fired. After a couple of goes it started. I would have to give it some sort of overhaul, but that was for the future. Now I could put the belt on to the bilge pump and let the engine do the work.

Once the boats were afloat again, I had a good look round. There were no leaks. It had been years of accumulated rainwater. I was satisfied with that, but the boats needed to dry out before I could live on one of them. It would be the back cabin of *Ariadne*.

We moved the boats to the towpath side of the canal, a couple of boat lengths from the lock entrance. I would be back the following day but now we walked back to the little house. Ma had made us a stew that we all sat down to at the table. Bobby had arrived home and we caught up with all the gossip, not that it took long. There was little or nothing to tell, except that the railways were long hours and very little in the way of pay.

I found the cigarettes in my backpack and gave them to Annie, and instantly made a friend for life. She had never had so many cigarettes at one time. I had been given 200 and she had those, less the twenty I had bartered for the bike. She seemed to do nothing but chain smoke. I settled into the front room and used my great coat as a blanket and turned in for the night.

I heard Bobby get up and go out to work at about four a.m. and then there was somebody coming into the room, closing the door quietly behind them. It was Annie. 'Move over, Jim. I'm cold and need you to warm me up.'

I couldn't believe that Annie would come to me as soon as Bobby had left for work. She reached out with her hands and they were really cold. Her flimsy, cotton nightie would never keep her warm. I relented, and she came to lie next to me.

'You can do me if you like,' she offered.

'What about Bobby?'

'Your Dad never complains.'

So there I had it. She gave Dad a regular shag and he never objected to anything she did around the house. I had no idea whether Mother ever knew. I was unlikely to find out.

'Just turn round and let me cuddle you and get you warm.'

She turned her back to me and I pulled her close to me. She was really chilled, but warmed up and I dozed. I had no idea whether Annie slept or not, but we were both woken up by a noise upstairs.

'I need to get up to see to Poppy,' she said, kissed my cheek and left me as silently as she had come.

I lay back, wondering what the hell was going on, but one thing that I was aware of was that I needed to be out of that house as soon as possible, and it would be today.

I was up and dressed first. Dad came into the kitchen to share a cup of tea with me.

'I'm moving out of here and going to live on the boats as soon as possible.'

'I don't blame you. It will be a cheap billet for you and you won't be that far away. Have you thought about getting a job?' he asked.

'No, I wanted to come and work with you on the boats but that's a non-starter. First things first, I need somewhere to live, and the boats are the best bet.'

'There are some things off the boat that I brought back here that you will need. I'll sort them out and bring them up to you later.'

That would be great and save me shopping around for simple basic things. I was collecting my things together when Dad asked, 'Did you get a visit from Annie this morning?'

'Yes, and she told me that she looked after you.'

'Did you take advantage of the situation?'

'No, but obviously you have.'

'Don't get on your high horse. It happened all the time on the cut. On a Saturday night, after a night at the pub, you might just find somebody else's wife in a quiet corner.'

'Did Mom know, and did she offer herself to somebody else?'

'I've no idea. I've never told her and never asked. That was years ago and has no relevance now.'

I recalled those far off Saturday nights at the canal pub. They had a song. I tried to remember the words. It went something like, *Keep your hands off, I know she squeezes absolutely fine, you can do what you like with anybody else's wife but keep your hands off – that's mine*, after which everybody would start laughing. Now I understood.

My opinion of my father was at an all-time low, and now being a frail elderly man was no excuse for his behaviour.

I pedalled furiously from the house in Rickmansworth to go to the boats. There was much to be done to get them dry and aired and watertight again. Part of that would be to get the battery charged, so that I wasn't reliant upon having to start the engine manually, which usually took two people.

I started with the engine, and ran that on tick over for the whole time that I was on the boats. They really needed new covers, but in the meantime, I would just make sure that they were fitted properly. Dad came later, bringing what he could carry. It was the first of several trips that I helped him with.

The last journey was to bring bedding, which I helped him with. Mother also came, to make sure that the bed was made properly and nothing was damp. She need not have worried. I had the cabin nice and cosy, with the stove being put to good use.

It had been a good day, and Mom insisted that I ate at home and didn't rely on going to the fish and chip shop. I would have to do some shopping the following day, when I had pots and pans to cook with and a plate and a dish to eat off. It was late when I returned to the boat and had a good night's sleep in familiar surroundings.

My one concern was what had happened to Mary Lee. I realised that Mr Mostrop was likely to know, and the following day saw me riding down to Bulls Bridge along the towpath. It took longer than I had expected, but it was still only mid-morning when I rode over the turnover bridge and knocked on Mr Mostrop's door and walked in. He looked up to see who his visitor was.

'Morning, Jim, everything alright?'

'Yes, thank you Mr Mostrop. I've found Mom and Dad and the boats. I really wanted to know what happened to Mary Lee.'

'Ah, I seem to remember you had a soft spot for her. I've some bad news for you, she married Danny Skinner and they went to live on the bank when the orders dried up.'

'Do you have an address for her?'

'Jim, I don't want you going round there to cause any trouble.'

'I just want to see her again. There won't be any trouble. It was all kids' stuff and I've had another life since then.'

'I'm sure you have. I think the army was good for you.'

'Do you have an address you could let me have, please?'

He looked over his glasses at me standing in the doorway. There was no anger in my eyes, just a recognition that I had lost my betrothed because of the army. The army had done me no favours that I could see. Mr Mostrop put down the papers he was holding and went to his filing cabinet and pulled out a card. He copied out the address on to a piece of paper that he handed to me. 'If anybody asks, I never gave you that piece of paper or where they lived. The street is just off the Commercial Road that crosses the Limehouse Cut.'

'No, Mr Mostrop, I will never say, and thank you.'

I left Mr Mostrop's office. The Limehouse Cut was closer to thirty miles, but on the flat on the bike I would make it by lunchtime, and so I did.

Coming off the cut on to the Commercial Road, I saw a postman and asked him. He directed me to the street and I found the number. I tentatively knocked. There was no answer. She could be out. She could have moved, and this was the wrong house. I had a thousand thoughts running through my head as I knocked for a second time. This time my knock was answered. The door was cracked open and whoever was inside just peered out.

'Mary, is that you?' I asked.

The door was opened wider, so that whoever was inside could have a better look at me and me at her. It was Mary. She was older, and it showed. She was wearing a chintz wrap-around overall with a child on her hip. The child was about two, in my reckoning, and had Mary's eyes and blond curly hair.

'Mary, I've come to find you.'

'Jim, whatever happened to you? You just disappeared and nobody knew anything.'

'I was tricked into signing on for five years in the army. That's where I've been. I heard that you married Danny.'

'Yes, and little Danny is his son and I'm now expecting another.'

'Why didn't you wait for me?'

'You just disappeared, and I might have had to wait for ever and still never see you again. Danny asked, and I said yes.'

'Mary, I'm still waiting for you. Leave Danny and come and live with me. I'm living on *Leo* and *Ariadne*. We could live together as we always planned. Bring the baby and the one you are expecting, and I'll bring them up as my own.'

'Jim, you are living in cloud cuckoo land. Do you have a job? I guess not. The boats and trade are dead. Danny has a good job working on the bins and we have a roof over our heads, you have nothing except a broken-down old boat. Five years ago, it would have been different, but now it's too little, too late.'

'I don't know what more to say to try to persuade you, but if that's your answer, I will have to respect it.'

'Jim, I don't want you hanging around here when Danny comes back. It would be trouble for me as well as you.'

I nodded my head. I realised the impossible position Mary was in.

'Bye, Mary, if you change your mind I'm moored up at Rickmansworth.'

'Jim, I will never change my mind.'

I turned and left. I climbed on my bike and rode along Euston Road. It was too far to ride back to Rickmansworth. I went into Euston Station and caught the local stopping train to Ricky and then only had the short distance back to the canal. I realised that I had lost the girl I had been betrothed to. The thought that I had been tricked into joining the army, and now the realisation that I had lost my childhood sweetheart, only made my thoughts even darker. Mentally I wasn't in a good place.

The following day I had a word with the lock keeper, who wasn't optimistic about keeping his job. I asked about boat yards that were still open, and most had closed down. There was one in Linslade. I decided to take the boat there and asked my Dad to come with me. It was the last trip that we ever had together.

At Linslade, they were converting carrying boats. They cut the boats in half, putting a new bow to the back end and new sterns on the front ends. They put cabins on as they made lodging for would-be holidaymakers. Who would want a holiday on the canal? The thought bemused me, but I could tie up at the yard provided. I paid them a monthly rate. It was more than I expected but it was a necessity. Going back to Germany for the AU car seemed further away than ever, as not only had I nowhere to keep it, but my money was being eaten into. What I really wanted was my own mooring and not to keep paying the boat yard where I was staying.

Things never seem to come in ones. At the boat yard, I met a guy called Andy who turned out to be a butcher. He had a really smart Jensen, straight from the showroom. He was keen to show me. It really was a great car and I was much impressed. He was in discussion with Mr Johnson, the yard's owner, about having a new boat built, but Mr Johnson was only interested in getting rid of the boats that he had as a result of his carrying fleet ceasing to trade. He had to look elsewhere. I had no idea why he wanted a newly-built boat.

It was at that time that the 'Towpath Telegraph' had a rumour that the Turvey yard at Cosgrove was closing down. Joe Turvey had retired and wound up the business. It got my grey matter working. A working yard might just be what I needed, and I rode my bike along the towpath to Cosgrove and yes, the rumour was correct, Mr Turvey had retired and the yard was just left lying idle. It was the ride back to Linslade that gave me the opportunity to sort out in my own mind what I needed to do to get the yard. If it was for sale, I didn't have enough money to buy it, or so I thought. I still had all my wages from the army, now in a metal box.

I had no idea but a trip to the British Transport Commission in London was needed. So the very next day I took my box of money and the train to Euston, and then made my way to their offices. After being sent from one department to another, I eventually found somebody that could help me. The yard was owned by BTC, and they were disappointed that Mr Turvey had retired as they had lost income from his rent. I offered to take over the lease. They wanted a new lease. I didn't really mind and settled for a 100-year lease at a peppercorn rent of just £10 a year. I opened up my savings box and counted out £1,000. Yes, I did have enough. A draft contract was prepared, and I left the offices after a very long day with the Cosgrove boat yard for 100 years. What I didn't know, or realise, was that there was a policy of closing down all the canals, and I would have a boat yard on a canal that didn't go anywhere and would be just a yard. They had taken my money and were probably laughing all the way to the bank. I was happy in my ignorance.

The next few days I collected all my things together to move on. That weekend Andy Brown, the guy with the Jensen, called in as he was out for a ride with his new girlfriend. I told him that I would be moving the boats to Cosgrove. He wanted to come with me and I needed another pair of hands to take the two boats, so, abandoning his girlfriend, we had a sunny Saturday taking the two boats to Cosgrove. Apart from me explaining the intricacies of boat handling and going through the locks, we had long discussions regarding engines, in particular marine engines. Andy was really enthusiastic about having his own boat built to exactly what he wanted. I thought what he really wanted was a yacht on the Med, and couldn't understand why he wanted an iron boat on the cut. For me it was a lifestyle, for Andy it was just a fantasy.

The boat yard was exactly what I wanted. There were wooden hovels built from old boats and most of the heavy gear was still there, including bostocks, winches, steam chest and a host of other items. Small hand tools had been taken and disposed of. Much to my surprise and pleasure, the telephone was still connected and there was a water closet, so that the days of 'bucket and chuck it' would be a thing of the past. I was happy tidying everything up and making it look as if it belonged to somebody.

I needed a job. Working on the yard was rewarding in one way, but not another. I decided to pay a visit to the local Labour Exchange in Newport, and what an experience that was. I was first told to wait in line with everybody else looking for work. I was eventually seen by a young girl.

'What's your name?' she asked.

'Jim James.'

'How long have you been unemployed?'

'Nearly two months.'

'What have you been doing since your last job?'

'I've never had a real job. I was in the army for five years and have just been demobbed.'

'And now you have no job and no income.'

'Can you find me a job?'

'I'll try. What did you do before you were called up, and what did you do in the army?'

'I worked with my Dad on the canal but that's all finished. In the army, I went to the cookhouse and peeled spuds.'

'You were a chef?'

'No, just a squaddie that peeled potatoes.'

'Oh, a catering assistant.'

'What do you have that I can do?'

'We don't have anything in the catering line at the moment. There might be an opening at a school kitchen, but it would only be part-time and there's no vacancy for a boatman. Here's a form, take it to the counter at the end and you will be given some money. You will need to come in here once a week to check that you are still unemployed and to collect your dole money.'

I was dismissed with a form. I went and stood in another queue. An hour later, I got to the front and was given some unemployment money. Outside I couldn't stop laughing. I was being paid to stay at home, on the yard with my boats and was being paid for doing just that. I could now go to Germany to collect my car.

It was a couple of weeks later that I took the train to London and then to Dover, and by train from Ostend then on to Hanover. It took a complete day. I made my way to Herr Maier's yard and slept in the AU overnight.

Hubert Maier wanted to know what I was doing in England, and wanted me to stay and work with him. I could stay on the yard until I found a place of my own and he would give me top wages. I thanked him for everything, but my destiny lay back in England with my family and getting my life back together. It was a reluctant farewell to Hubert and Germany as I drove my AU back to England.

I was expecting some difficulty, but during my last weeks at Hanover I had found out that many of the men, particularly the officers, had bought German cars and had registered them on the base so that they were effectively new British cars. I did the same and my AU had a British number plate, I had the log book, army insurance and was able to bring my car back to the UK without customs even looking at my documentation.

I broke my journey back by way of Wuppertal, to see the Schwenkar family. They were pleased to see me and insisted that I stayed the night, so that over and after dinner, I told them my story and that I was now driving back home. Helga was married to Wolf and was expecting her first child, and Heinz and his girlfriend were now engaged and looking forward to getting married. Heinz would take the pig business over when Papa retired, but I guessed that he would always be on the yard doing something.

It was a fond farewell to the Schwenkar family as I completed the journey to Calais. The journey had taken two days before I put the AU into the largest of the hovels and covered it over with a tarpaulin. Andy came round that weekend to find me cleaning my AU. He was not only impressed, but wanted me to take him out for a drive. It was fun being able to show off my car to my new friend. It used so much petrol that it would only go out on special occasions.

So, my life was moving into a new regular routine. I would go to the Labour Exchange once a week, and to Rickmansworth on Sundays with a rabbit or pheasant or a hare or something else I managed to catch for a day with the family. I didn't stay and always came back to the boats, which I was working on full-time. They were looking really good and would have passed as the best turned-out working boats on the canal, worthy of belonging to a Number One.

Word had been passed around that I knew about diesel engines and I started to have a steady stream of boats that needed attention. There was little or nothing to go wrong with them, but having constant running, they eventually needed to be re-bored with over size pistons fitted, new valves to get good compression and the oil pump serviced. Since there were no garages on the canal, when you had a boat you either had to do the work yourself of find a boat yard where the engine could be taken out and the factory engineer brought out to do the work. Using my yard and expertise was favoured. I didn't know what to charge, and left it to the people coming to pay me what they thought over and above the cost of any parts. It worked well. I made more friends that way and there were always a couple of boats tied up at the yard waiting my attention.

Andy had found a boat builder in Weedon and had a hull made to his specification and a cabin fitted. He wanted me to fit his engine, and asked my advice regarding what engine he should buy. I suggested that the small AU marine engine would never let him down and with a 2:1 ratio gearbox would swing a large propeller with more than enough thrust for him. When the boat was on the water, floating, we went with *Leo* to Weedon to bring it back to Cosgrove, being towed behind and locked breasted up. It was a fun trip and I could see why Andy had been hooked on boats and canal boats in particular.

He wanted me to sort out the AU engine for him, so the following Monday morning, I rode my bike into Fenny Stratford where AU had recently opened a new showroom and warehouse. It was a most impressive building, being all glass at the front. I left my bike outside and went into the showroom. The salesman I met had no idea about marine engines, as all he wanted to do was sell cars. I took some leaflets. I would need to translate them and read them back in Cosgrove.

I was standing near the showroom doors when I heard a large limo drive up to the front door. I was sure that it was running a bearing on one of the front wheels. It was not my problem, but after years of listening to vehicles come into the Hanover workshops I could spot the problem from twenty yards. This skill had not deserted me.

Three executives got out of the car and pushed me out of the way to go into the showroom. They were speaking in German, saying how awful the English were; untidy, disorganised and downright rude. My hackles were raised by this tirade and I confronted them to address them in German.

*'Gentlemen, can I say that I think your comments are unwarranted and speaking in a language that you think won't be understood, you are not only*

*mistaken but are extremely rude and you should be ashamed.'*

They were taken aback that somebody more or less off the street should address them in fluent German.

*'What is a German doing here in England?'* one of them asked.

*'I am English and angry that you have insulted me, not expecting me to understand. I have heard every word of your conversation and have understood everything that you have said. The British are in awe of the quality of German engineering and it is your lack of understanding and organisational skills that these premises are not to your liking. Anyway, I wish you luck in trying to get the car you came in back to Germany. I doubt that you will get as far as Dover.'*

*'Why what's wrong with it? It's a new car and the top of our range.'*

*'What sort of advert would it be for you to return with it on the back of a breakdown truck?'*

*'That will never happen.'*

*'I beg to differ. Let me change the bearing for you. You can go into the stores and hope that you can find a replacement while I go home to get my tools.'*

They had nothing to say. I guessed what they wanted was to prove me wrong. I went to my bike and rode back to Cosgrove to get my pre-war AU convertible from the hovel, and put the tools I needed into the boot and drove back to Fenny, drawing up outside the front door, leaving it alongside their new limo.

*'Where did you get that?'* they exclaimed, as they looked at my highly polished red monster of a car.

*'My business.'*

*'We only ever made less than twenty of that model and not one survived the war.'*

*'This one did, and I found it, restored it and it is registered in my name. Now did you find your bearing?'*

*'Yes, here it is.'*

I was given the wheel bearing. I found a jack and lifted the front of the car, removed the wheel, brakes, steering and then the bearing. It took some removing but then I hammered on the new bearing, restoring everything back to working order. I went to show them the worn bearing, handing it to them.

*'Take this back, and take up with your supplier why are they supplying poor quality parts to your most prestigious car.'*

They had no idea what to say, other than to invite me into their office to offer me a coffee and express their apologies. I accepted their invitation and the apology.

Sitting in their office, we reverted to speaking in English. They were fluent and only then did they realise that I wasn't lying. They wanted to know about my car. They had been supplied to the hierarchy of Hitler's close associates and I could name my own price, as they wanted my car in their museum in Karlsruhr. I declined their offer, as I told them how I had found it and restored it while I was working in the motor pool in Hanover. They were most impressed, and surprised that I was effectively unemployed now that I was back in Blighty.

I left, thanking them for the coffee, shaking their hands to return to the red AU that had attracted a small crowd of people out of the depot. I ignored them, started the monster up and left with a roar in a cloud of blue smoke. The wheels spun on the tarmac as I gunned the accelerator. It would be a lasting memory of me and their visit to England.

I went back to the yard, and over the next few days sorted out the engine and gearbox that Andy needed for his new boat. I rode my bike back to the AU outlet and ordered what Andy needed. They would give me a call when the engine arrived from Karlsruhr. I wondered how they would deliver it. There was no way that I could carry it on my bike, and it would never go anywhere near my car. I would wait for their call.

It was a couple of weeks later that I took a call from a lady at the garage. Could I call round the following day at about ten o'clock. I thought it strange that they wanted me to call at a particular time, but I dismissed it as some sort of import requirement.

The following day I rode down to the depot on my bike, parked it outside the parts department, but was asked to go into the main reception and report there. It was all very strange. I walked around the building and introduced myself to the receptionist.

'Mr James, you are expected.'

She picked up the internal telephone, spoke to somebody and smiled as she replaced the receiver. 'If you care to wait, Mrs Hargreaves will take you through.'

I was even more confused. All I wanted was to make arrangements for the delivery of Andy's marine engine.

After a few minutes, a slim lady in a skirted business suit came and shook my hand.

'Mr James, thank you for coming in this morning. My name's Ingrid Hargreaves.'

'Pleased to meet you,' was all that I managed to say. Ingrid had a fair complexion with sparkling blue eyes and hair that cascaded over her shoulder. She really was a lovely looking lady, and I followed her into a meeting room with a highly polished table where there were matching high-backed chairs around. There were three men sitting behind the table with papers in front of them. I had been here before, twice in fact. The first was the interrogation by Lt Col Bridge, who had sent me to the cookhouse as a potential troublemaker, and the second time was also with Bridge as I face the accusation of burying Corporal Hunter. I was instantly on my guard as to what this was all about. It certainly had nothing to do with a diesel engine.

'Mr James, thank you for coming in. Please take a seat, and can I offer you a coffee?' the middle man asked.

I shook my head and just stood looking at them. All my self-confidence had evaporated, as I was back in the army, being interrogated by Germans this time.

'Please, Mr James, we would like to interview you for a post here, working in the stores and workshops.'

'Don't want a job,' I muttered. I was suspicious of everything. I had been tricked once before, and was on my guard about being tricked again by clever people who could read and write better than me.

'You haven't heard what we have to offer.'

'Don't want a job,' I repeated.

'Mr James, we have spoken to Major Black at Hanover and he was disappointed that you didn't want to stay on in the army, to continue with running the stores that you put in place and running the workshops. He was putting you in line for promotion through the ranks.'

'Hated the army and everybody in it,' I responded.

'That didn't appear to be the case. We also went to see Hubert Maier and he sang your praises as being the best worker and engineer he had ever had, and I think that he saw you as taking over his business when he retired. You were like a son to him.'

'Herr Maier is a good man. I wanted to be here in England, back with my family.'

'Yes, he told us that as well. Why are you presently unemployed?'

'Don't want a job,' I repeated again. 'Can I go now?'

The three men looked to each other.

'Mr James, you haven't heard our offer yet.'

'I don't want to be here. I just want to collect my engine.'

At that point Mrs Hargreaves intervened and spoke to the interviewing group. She spoke in German.

*'Let me have a private word with Herr James. Something about this interview has upset him.'*

*'Please, if it will help. I can't believe that we have intimidated him.'*

Mrs Hargreaves turned to me. 'Mr James, could I have a word, please?'

I nodded my approval and she took my arm as we went into the anteroom.

'Mr James, there is no need to be afraid. Herr Schwindling wants to help you, not punish you. Did you have a bad experience in the army being interviewed?'

'They tricked me into signing on for five years, instead of being rejected as I couldn't read or write. They saw me as a troublemaker and I spent the first year on fatigues in the cookhouse. In there, they are just like the people in the army.'

'No, they are not, believe me. They think that you are the best person to have walked through those doors ever since they opened the depot. They want to offer you the top job. You would have a free hand to do whatever you wanted, and everybody here would have to do as you say, and you wouldn't be beholden to anybody. Herr Schwindling is the top man in Germany. What he says goes, and he wants you and wants to be your friend. You just tell him what you are doing and that's all.'

I was quiet as she told me this. I had no idea what to say. I was totally confused.

'I still can't read or write very well, and I never learnt to count as Dad always looked after the money.'

'Mr James, Jim, I will work for you and will do all the reading and writing that needs to be done. You do what you are good at doing and I'll do what I'm good at doing.'

I mellowed under her reassuring smile. She put her hand on my arm. 'Jim, it will be alright, believe me.'

I just my nodded my understanding.

'Can we go back and listen to what they have to say?'

Again, I just nodded my acceptance.

She took my arm and led me back into the meeting.

*'He had a bad experience being interrogated in the army. I think that you can make him the job offer now.'*

'Thank you, Ingrid.' Herr Schwindling then turned to me and addressed me in perfect English.

'Mr James, I want you to come to work for me personally. I want you to turn this part of our organisation into a showroom for the world. I know that you can do it. You know that you can do it. So why don't we just do it?'

'What would I have to do?'

'Organise the stores as you did in Hanover and sort out the workshops.'

'How would I do that?'

'Mr James, you would be the head man here. Your only boss would be me, and I'm over in Germany and don't ever want to come here again. Whatever you want, you would just have to pick up the phone and ask me.'

'You know that I can hardly read or write.'

'Yes, we know all about that, and Ingrid will be by your side so that you won't have to read or write anything. Your skills lie in a different direction. So, what do you say?'

'Seems too good to be true.'

'It probably is but I'm willing to take the chance.'

'If I can't do the job, I would just call you and tell you, and I could go back to what I'm doing now?'

'Yes, if that's the only condition. I think that you would be honest with me and that also makes a refreshing change, as most people tell me what they think I want to hear.'

'In that case, I will see how we get on.'

'When can you start?'

'Whenever. Next Monday, if that's alright with you?'

Herr Schwindling stood up and came round the table to me. He was taller that I had imagined. He had a full head of hair that was cut short and combed. He was dressed in a dark suit that looked expensive. He held out a hand that had a soft texture that had a strength about it.

I took it in mine, and I realised that this man with pale blue eyes and tanned complection, he and I would become friends, good friends. He seemed to be a man of his word, and in this company his word was the last and only word.

'Jim, you haven't asked about pay,' he said, as he held on to my hand.

'Herr Schwindling, I'm taking the job to do what's needed and not for the money.'

'That's what I thought. Do a good job for me and I'll look after you.'

'Thank you, I think that you will.'

I turned and walked out with Ingrid Hargreaves.

'Jim, thank you for saying yes. Herr Schwindling has taken a liking to you and there is nobody in the company that will go against him. I am looking forward to working with you.'

'Mrs Hargreaves, how come a German lady speaks perfect English and is working here in Fenny?'

She smiled. 'Yes, I am German, from Osnabruck. I met an English officer, got married and I have two children. He was posted here in England and I came with him. I managed to get this job because I am bilingual in English and German.'

'Sorry, I didn't mean to be inquisitive about your personal life.'

'Jim, sometime you need to tell me about your family, and why you are here in Fenny.'

'Maybe, and maybe not. Thank you for talking me round. I will be here first thing on Monday.'

'We will expect you. Don't worry, everything will be alright.'

I left the offices and rode my bike back to Cosgrove, wondering what I had taken on. I had no idea why I had accepted their offer. I had a day of not settling to do anything and an even more restless night, unable to sleep. I must have been mad.

The days dragged. I needed a better suit than the one that the army had provided for me when I was demobbed. I went into Stony Stratford and bought a better suit, some shirts and a tie. I had never worn a shirt and tie before I was in the army, or since, but being in charge of the new AU depot, I thought that I needed to look the part. I spent the evening pressing the shirts. I would go to work on the bike and get changed when I got there. That was the plan and I would see how it worked out.

The marine engine arrived and was delivered to my yard, and I pulled Andy's boat out and set about installing it. It was a welcome distraction over the weekend. Andy came round on Saturday to 'help'. He made tea and helped me to drink it. Another weekend would see the job finished. I didn't mention the fact that I had taken a job. Having a Sunday at home with Mom and Dad, I told them that I had been offered a job with AU in Fenny. They were pleased, and Bobby was relieved as he could see his wage supporting me as well as Annie and Mom and Dad.

Dad was interested in my job. I told him that I was working in the stores and the workshop. He didn't press exactly what the job entailed, but was pleased for me. I was pleased to get out of the questioning.

I had managed to curry favour with Annie, as each and every Sunday, when I turned up, I gave her a packet of twenty Woodbines that brought a smile to her lips. I guessed that she never offered them around and kept them all to herself. I also guessed that Bobby never knew.

# CHAPTER SEVEN

### *Starting a new job*

I remember well my first morning at work. I rode my bike and arrived about six in the morning, and was not surprised to find that the only person there was the security guard, who was very suspicious seeing me arrive on my bike. He let me into the boiler room, where I changed into my suit. He walked around with me. The stores were a shambles, which was no more than I expected. The workshops were dirty and had never been cleaned since the building had been taken over. The mechanics had just left the tools where they had dropped them after finishing the job they were doing. In the showroom, everywhere looked neat and tidy, as I guessed the cleaners had been in overnight. I eventually found my office. It had my name on the door:

Jim James
Depot Manager

I was both surprised and embarrassed. In the office was a large desk, together with an executive type chair, two other chairs facing the desk, a coffee table off to one side with a couch and two easy chairs that formed an informal area for more casual discussions. I guessed I would never use them, or the desk for that matter, but I was impressed. On the wall were photographs of several models and also a picture of the first car and first production line. This was the centre of my empire.

One of the features of my office was that it was located between the workshops and the showroom, so that I could overlook both, and likewise they could see me watching them. The first people to arrive were the mechanics, who just meandered in, waiting for orders to start work. The manager had his own office and just sat there with a mug of tea looking through the work schedules. That would have to change.

It was around nine o'clock when the salesmen started to arrive and just sat around drinking tea and coffee, smoking and reading papers, waiting for somebody to walk through the door. That would also have to change.

It was after half past nine when Ingrid arrived and looked a bit flushed when she saw that I was already there. She came in to see me.

'Good morning, Jim, you don't mind me calling you Jim?'

'Why did you come in at nine-thirty when everybody else came in at nine?'

She blushed.

'I had to take the children to nursery for nine and that's why I'm late. I'm sorry. If it's a problem, I'll make alternative arrangements in future.'

'It's not a problem. I just need to know. You don't have to make any changes to what you are presently doing.'

She smiled. 'Thank you. I can see that you have already taken on the mantel of being the manager.'

'Being a sergeant in the army served me well in giving orders, but not necessarily taking them. Tell me, what do I need to do?'

'I will collect the morning's post and we can go through them together. Any action required I will deal with. At the end of the day, you can read the mail, sign it and I will see that it's posted.'

'Ingrid, I will not read anything and will never ever sign anything. You will have to sign it for me.'

'If that's what you want.'

'That's exactly what I want, and I don't want to ever see a piece of paper on my desk. Everything has its place and paper either hits the bin or the filing cabinet.'

'That's clear enough. We have a lady come in every morning to do the filing.'

'Is there anything else?' I asked.

'There are a couple of things. You will need to give your National Insurance number to the accounts. I will do that for you if you have the letter from the Labour Exchange. You will also need to give me your bank details, as your wages will be paid directly into your account. Nobody here will ever have sight of how much you earn, and that includes me.'

'I don't have a bank account.'

'Can I suggest that will be your first priority?'

'You can suggest that, but it's not first on the list. Can you arrange for the sales manager and the workshop manager to see me in fifteen minutes, and then we can go through the post?'

'Yes, Mr James, I will do that straight away,' she said, as she turned and left.

It amused me. I was Jim when she arrived late and Mr James as she left. I preferred Jim, but whatever, I was not concerned.

I had the two managers knock the door and present themselves to me. I sat on the edge of the desk with both men standing before me. The sales manager was Geof Smith, and was rather portly with cigarette ash resting on his tie that fell on to his rather rotund midriff. The workshop manager was tall and slim, and was wearing a pair of overalls that I guessed he had worn the previous week as they had grease and oil stains. I started with him.

'Mr Jenkins, your appearance is a disgrace and the state of the workshops does you no credit either. From now until the end of the month, all workshop personnel will wear clean overalls every day. To start with they will be dark blue. I am having the workshop floor painted and when that is completed, the mechanics will all wear white overalls and the floor and work surfaces will be clean, tidy and all the tools put away as and when they have been used.'

Jenkins just laughed. 'You have to be kidding me. This lot will do as they want, and white overalls, I ask you. This is a garage, not a hospital.'

'Jenkins, you are dismissed. I object to you and your attitude. This is exactly what it is; it is a car hospital where broken vehicles come to be repaired and serviced and returned to their owners in showroom condition. You can go, and go now. I don't want to see your face here again.'

Jenkins's jaw dropped. He had no response to my tirade. He just turned and left. I would need to sort out his severance pay later. The sales manager was moving from one foot to the other, wondering what was in store for him.

'Mr Smith, the showroom is a disgrace and so is your appearance. I wouldn't buy anything from you. Just smarten up. As for the showroom, the cleaners come each evening and by nine-thirty your salesmen have made such a mess as to have made the cleaners' work irrelevant. I will stop the cleaners and get your salesmen to not only clean the cars but polish the floor and clean the windows, if I don't see an improvement. Concentrate on welcoming people into the showroom, give them tea or coffee and biscuits. You will also need to have a couple of apprentices at your beck and call. I don't want to see any other sort of make of car on the forecourt. If a customer comes in any other make, they are to be taken around the back, washed, polished and valeted before being returned to their owners. Have you got all of that?'

'Yes, Mr James. You will see an improvement. I will see to it personally.'

'Thank you, Mr Smith. All I want is for you to sell as many cars as you can, to try to outstrip our allocation. I'm sure that you can do it.'

'I'll make sure that we do. Thank you,' he said, as he almost ran from my office, just glad to get out of my range of fire.

Ingrid came in with a bundle of papers in her hand and a smile on her lips.

'Do you have anything to tell me?' she asked.

'Such as?'

'Why did you sack Jenkins?'

'He was dirty and insolent. I won't tolerate either.'

Again, she smiled a disarming smile. 'I promise not to do either.'

'Now, tell me what you've got for me.'

'Just the post and a few other outstanding things.'

'Just read them to me.'

'Can I sit down?'

'Please, I'm sorry. Take a seat. I don't think that I will ever sit behind a desk, and if you want a tea or coffee break you just need to ask, as I will never want either while I'm at work but I don't want to deny you.'

She gave me a curious look, sat down and started reading the first of the letters. It needed some sort of response. I asked her what I needed to say. She just suggested a rather non-committal answer, that I told her to write and then read it to me, before she signed it in my name before posting.

This seemed to be the pattern. I gave her a fifteen-minute break halfway through the morning and I went to the boiler room to meet the maintenance man. We shared a cup of tea together. The word had already got out about me sacking Jenkins. He was a slob and ran the workshops in exactly the same way as he ran his life. Everybody was now on full alert regarding me and their jobs.

· What I had learnt in the army was that top brass always thought they knew how the base was run, but if you asked the maintenance man, he would tell you exactly how the base was run and this was no exception. I asked him who was the best young guy in the workshop. The answer came back Bill Ellis. He was young and smart and knew cars and their workings inside out. He had just got married and needed all the money he could get his hands on. He would be my man.

Back in the office, Ingrid was waiting for me. We returned to going through the mail, and I was pleased when that was finished. She got up to go back to her office to start typing up the mail when I asked her to send Bill Ellis up to see me. She wondered how I knew Bill Ellis. She would have to go on wondering.

It was a little later that Bill Ellis presented himself to me. He was just as the boiler man and told me. He was young and smart and about my age.

'Come in, Bill. Relax if you can. You know that I got rid of Jenkins this morning, and it stops there.'

'Yes, I don't think anybody liked him and were pleased to see the back of him.'

I guessed that he had a few fiddles going as well that nobody was supposed to know anything about, but I put that thought to one side. 'Did you do National Service?' I asked.

'Yes, did my two years in the REME.'

'Lucky you. I had a year in the cookhouse peeling spuds. Did you do your training here or somewhere else?'

'Did an apprenticeship with a dealership that hit the buffers in the early '50s and I was lucky to get this job.'

'I need you to do me a favour.'

'Ask away, if I can't do it I'll tell you.'

'I want you to manage the workshop. You can have a raise up to what Jenkins was earning and you can start now.'

'And that's me doing you a favour?'

'Yes, I'm army trained and you know all about that; if it moves salute it, if it doesn't, paint it. I want you to get the garage floor painted a pastel colour over a weekend when we can close the workshop of vehicles.'

'Paint the floor!'

'Yes, I don't want to see any mess. Oil spills are to be cleaned up immediately. When the floor is nice and clean, I want all the men to have clean white overalls, fresh on every day. I want to give an impression that we are the best; we are the best and need to tell people. As for tools, put them away clean, ready for the next job. You might need to recruit more apprentices to do that and also have two at the behest of Geof Smith. He will tell you all about having nothing but clean cars in the showroom and out on the forecourt.'

'That sounds real army. Don't tell me you were a bastard sergeant.'

'Only on the surface, underneath I'm really horrible.'

This raised a smile on Bill's face.

'There is one thing that irritated me this morning when I saw all the guys arrive, and that was they didn't seem to know what to do. It will be your workshop and you can organise who does what where and when, but you could start the day with finishing off the jobs started the previous afternoon that weren't finished. As and when the service vehicles come in, you could start those during the morning, putting off the repairs until late afternoon and early mornings. I'm hoping to get the stores on a better footing so that we will be able to pull spares from there, and not wait for them to be delivered from Karlsruhr.'

'That's our biggest hold up. Sometimes we have to wait a couple of weeks for a part.'

'That's something for me to work towards. That's it, Bill. Let's get things moving.'

Bill left my office happier that when he had been summoned. It was time for me to start attacking the stores. It would be some task, but not one I shirked from. They couldn't be any worse than the army stores in Hanover.

There was another person that I needed to see, and I had no idea that he existed until I put my head round the door that was marked 'Accounts'. Behind the desk that was covered with bits of paper sat a dapper, middle-aged man with white hair and a healthy tanned face.

'Who are you?' I asked.

'You can just call me Fred. I keep you honest as best I can. I see that you've already got rid of some of the riff-raff that we have here. I need your bank details to send on to the guys in Karlsruhr.'

'So, who's your boss?'

'You are, but can I ask you to keep the sacking that side of the door and not in here. I need the money, as my annual golf fees are increasing alarmingly every year.'

'Fred, I have to confess that I can't count very well above three or four and I have no understanding of money, as my Dad always dealt with that. All I need to know is when we have had a bad week, month, year, which means that we will all be looking for a job. If I don't hear from you, I will take it as good news.'

Fred just sat back and had a second look at me, wondering how somebody who couldn't add up had the top job. What he didn't realise was that I didn't need to. He would do it for me and Ingrid would do all the reading and writing. I had arrived in my perfect job.

So my first day set the format for each and every day that followed. I would arrive early and leave late on my bike, getting changed in the boiler room. I would take my letters at nine-thirty and have them read back to me at four. Between times I spent in the stores and making out requisitions for items that were missing. Slowly, we had an almost full compliment of items that were on regular demand. Bill Ellis had the workshop floor painted and the mechanics fitted with white overalls, looking smart and professional. There was not a dirty vehicle on the site, as more apprentices were appointed and set about cleaning anything and everything. Sales also picked up as shiny new models were wheeled into the showroom and then driven out of the lot. Even Geof Smith looked more presentable and smoking was only done at the rear of the premises, as there was now an area with a coffee machine for customer use only. It was put to good use. I was pleased with my efforts at management.

On a more domestic level, I went to the bank in Stony Stratford to open an account and put all my army money in to start it off. I would go in on a Saturday morning to withdraw a few pounds, but Ingrid told me to keep receipts of everything so that I could claim the money back. That would also go directly into my account.

I still went to see Mom and Dad on Sundays for lunch, and I gave Mom a £5 note while nobody was looking. She didn't want to take it, but she always did. I thought that if I told everybody that I was the boss at AU, Bobby might want to come to work with me. I realised that nepotism didn't work and could split families, should I ever have to sack him for whatever reason, and I was sure that there would be several reasons that I hadn't even imagined. I left it that I just worked in the stores and everybody seemed happy.

On Saturdays and evenings, I worked on fitting and servicing canal boat engines. A former worker on the yard turned up, it was Old Dick who had worked there for nigh-on forty years. He did a deal with Andy to fit out the boat. Dick worked wonders with wood and was a true craftsman. Andy paid him £2 an hour and I gave him the run of the yard. I liked the idea that somebody was there during the day and we worked side by side on Saturday mornings, and we chewed over the 'good old days' when boating was taken seriously.

I was attracted to Ingrid. She really was lovely and her husband was a lucky man. I wondered if she would move as and when he was given a new posting, but evidently he was only an adjutant and his brigadier now had a desk job in Whitehall, and it was a nine-to-five job, five days a week. He wasn't going anywhere and was just working out his time in the service. He commuted, and Ingrid had a job that I hoped she liked and would stay in.

Sometimes I just wondered, as she read letters to me or took dictation, as her skirt rode up over her knee or she wore a see-through white blouse so that I had a good view of her white lace bra, but I put any lecherous thoughts out of my mind. She was married with two children, and I was not about to upset that applecart by doing something stupid like coming on to her.

# CHAPTER EIGHT

## *A strange encounter*

The weeks passed. The months passed. I had more clothes than I had ever had in my life. Dick had put a full-length cabin on *Ariadne* and a new cratch on *Leo*, and I paid him £2 an hour and covered the cost of any materials he needed. He may have extended the hours, I never checked up on him and I guessed that he wouldn't bite the hand that fed him. I think that he just liked being on the yard doing things. He almost had his own little business fitting out boats that seemed to come and go. It was a mutually beneficial arrangement.

There was one incident that I need to relate. One afternoon I returned to my office, for Ingrid to go through the letters she had written for me. When she came into the office she was quite flustered.

'What's happened?' I asked.

'We have gypsies camping on the edge of the forecourt, where there's a bit of grass.'

I went to the window and yes, there were two vans and some piebald horses. That was strange. They normally didn't get this close to civilisation. I would go and talk to them to see what the problem was.

As I turned round, Ingrid was picking up the telephone.

'What are you doing?' I asked.

'Calling the police to get them moved.'

I put my hand on the phone, stopping the call. 'Phone the police and you are fired, here and now. I will deal with this in my own way.'

I took the receiver off her and replaced it on its cradle. She looked at me, shocked at my reaction, and couldn't believe that I had threatened her with her job for doing what she thought was the right thing to do. I was angry that she had made the decision for me. I would talk to the gypsies. I turned away from Ingrid and went out to confront them.

There were two gypsy families, or maybe just one. I would find out. There was an elderly couple and a younger couple. The younger of the men was dark-haired and slim with a weathered face already. He turned to look at me as I approached. I couldn't believe it. It was Jonny Smith, my blood brother, from when we were kids fighting on the towpath over his horse.

I stopped a few feet away from him and we faced each other. I spoke first. 'Jonny Smith, don't you recognise me? I'm Jim James, your blood brother.'

I held up my left had to show him the scar on my thumb. He just dropped whatever was in his hand and leapt at me as our arms embraced each other.

'Jim, I haven't seen you in a long time.'

'No, the army took me for five years.'

Jonny turned to his parents to explain. 'Dad, Ma, this is Jim James. We became blood brothers after a fight on the canal.' He turned to me. 'Do you still have your knife?'

'I'm never without it,' I said, as I released the knife from its sheath and offered it to him. I received another hug before he took me and my knife to show his father the scars on our thumbs. He greeted the news with grave suspicion.

'Mr Smith, Mrs Smith,' I said, greeting them with respect.

Jonny was just pleased to see me. 'This is Alice my wife, and our little boy. I've called him Jim, after you.'

'Mrs Smith,' were my only words at the introduction. 'Jonny, you can't stay here. They want to call the police.'

'It's the same everywhere these days. Wherever we pull up, we are moved on. We are on our way to Appleby but one of the horses has either cut himself on some barbed wire or somebody has cut him.'

We walked over to look at the horse. He had a bad cut and needed urgent attention.

'Is he slowing you down?' I asked.

Jonny just nodded. 'We wintered in Kent after the fruit picking, and we are now running out of days.'

I thought for a moment. 'Jonny, I have a boat yard where you can stay as long as you like. Nobody will trouble you. It's at Cosgrove, on the canal, where I live on my boat. Get yourself together and on the road to the Stony roundabout at the Northampton turn, and wait for me. I will see you there to take you the last mile to my yard.'

'Jim, are you sure about this?'

'Jonny, you are family, my brother. You have plenty of time and I'll see you at the Northampton turn. Now, I have to get back to stop them calling the police.'

I turned and left them as Jonny explained things to his parents.

Back in the office, Ingrid was waiting for me, standing with her arms folded, about to confront me.

'You are a gypsy!' was her simple statement, which evidently explained everything to her.

'Of sorts, yes. They are moving on without your interference or involving the police. As far as you are concerned, the matter is over.'

'Herr Schwindling will not be happy over this.'

'Who will tell him, because it won't be me.'

'Are you threatening me?'

'No, I would never threaten you. I would just walk out and let you explain to Erich Schwindling why I left you and the company. I don't want this any more than you, and what I am or what I've been, I can't change any of that, and it's all behind me. You do as you please, you will anyway.'

'I can't believe that you are a gypsy.'

'What's wrong with gypsies? That man out there is my blood brother,' I said, showing her the scar on my thumb. 'Being my brother, he comes before you and your precious company. They are going because I asked them to in a respectful manner and they will go. It is no longer an AU problem. If you have a problem with that, you need to deal with it.'

She turned and walked out, leaving me with a pile of post on my desk. I picked them up and put them in the waste basket. I left the office and went to the boiler house, changed into my boating clothes and rode my bike to Stony Stratford, to wait for Jonny and the caravans.

When Jonny turned up, they followed me to the boat yard, where I opened up the gates and went in. I closed and locked the gates behind them. They would not be disturbed while staying with me.

I went on to *Ariadne*, lit the stove and made a large kettle of tea. I went to where they were setting up camp and we sat around drinking my tea. We were breaking down barriers. I explained the demise of the canal travelling families and they told me about the difficulties that they were facing. We both came from communities that were under threat from the establishment.

They were fascinated by me living on the boat and Mrs Smith came on board so that I could show her the back cabin where I lived. It was like a floating caravan that she was familiar with.

That evening, I was invited to share their evening meal. I took my enamel plate and they served up some sort of stew that I ate with my little knife. I fitted in to their way of life, or was it that they fitted into mine?

After dinner, I had a long talk with Jonny. I showed him where I kept the key to the gates so that they could come and go as they pleased. I also persuaded him to leave the horse with me. I would call the vet to see to the horse and I would keep him fit while they were up in Appleby. He could call and collect him whenever it suited him. He would tell his father and it was settled.

Mr Smith came to thank me and told me that Mrs Smith would give me a reading before they left, and so she did. She took my hand and smiled back to me. 'You will have a long and happy life. I can see there will be a major problem along the way, but you will overcome that and will also have a family that will give you great joy. Jim, I wish you well and give you a good luck blessing. You are a good man and you will always be part of our family.'

'Thank you, Mrs Smith. I didn't really want any bad news.'

She left me and when I awoke next morning, they had already gone, leaving me with the injured horse. I didn't go into work. They could do without me for a day. I called out the vet, who came round in the afternoon to look at the injured horse. He put on a dressing and gave him an injection. He would call again and said to call him if the horse got worse or suffered in any way. I would have to make arrangements to be on hand as and when he called again.

It was the following day that I went back to my routine of going in at six in the morning on the bike, getting changed into my suit before going into the stores, workshop, showroom and eventually into my office. I had a short wait before Ingrid came in to see me.

'I'm sorry about my outburst the other day.' She gave her apology. 'When you didn't come in yesterday, I thought that you had just walked out and left.'

'I had other things to attend to.'

'What happened to the post I left for you?'

'I'm giving you a verbal warning. If you ever do that again I will fire you.'

'What did I do to deserve that?'

'Left paper in my office.'

'What did you do with it? It was important.'

'If it was that important why did you leave it? The very day I started, I told you that paper was either to be put in the waste bin or filed.'

'Did you have it filed?'

'No, it hit the waste bin that the cleaners emptied.'

'Jim, that wasn't necessary.'

'What happened to Mr James? It seems as if familiarity has bred contempt. It was your responsibility that you neglected. This is your second warning in three days. I will expect your resignation by the end of the week.'

'Are you sacking me?'

'No, you are resigning with no chance of a reference from me at least.'

'Jim, Mr James, why are you so mean to me?'

'Work it out for yourself. You can send in another shorthand typist to go through the post for your last two days.'

'There's nobody else that can read German.'

'Ingrid, send in your replacement. Let me worry about that.'

Ingrid left looking down at the carpet, wondering where everything had gone so wrong. All I wanted was an apology and there was nothing coming from Ingrid in that direction. She would have to apologise or go.

A few minutes later a young girl, I guessed in her late teens, came in looking anxious and quite fearful.

'What's your name?' I asked.

'Pam.'

'Well, Pam, I'm not going to eat you, all I want is for you to read the incoming mail and make notes to write a reply for me.'

She looked from me to the first of the letters and started reading it to me. It was a letter of little consequence. I told her to have it filed as we moved on to the next. About an hour later we had been through all the post and she left to type up the answers. I went and changed into white overalls and spent the rest of the day in the stores. HQ continued to bring out new cars, with an ever-increasing number of component parts that needed numbering and putting into store. I guessed that it would never stop.

I had a surprise call from Erich Schneidling, asking me to go to Karlsruhr for the following Tuesday as there was a heads of operations meeting and it was important that I went. I had little option but to agree.

I spent an hour on the telephone sorting out flights to Strasbourg, and then hired car so that I could get to and from Karlsruhr. I would find accommodation when I arrived, probably at the airport.

I had more or less finished telephoning when Ingrid knocked and came in to see me.

'Mr James, I would like to apologise for not adhering to your instructions and for being familiar with you.'

'Thank you. I accept your apology. I'm hoping that we can move on from this on a more professional basis.'

'I will do as you ask and not try to interfere in future.'

'Ingrid, the matter is closed and behind us.'

'Do you still want me to tender my resignation? I have already typed it out,' she said, as she gave me an envelope.

I tore it up. 'When I want you to leave, you won't have to resign.'

'Thank you. You really are the best boss I've ever had and I've been upset that I made you angry with me.'

'It was only feigned anger. I have intolerance to anything to do with typed paper. It will pass. I was once asked to sign a document that I couldn't read. I was tricked into signing it and it cost me five years peeling potatoes in the army. I hate both paper and the army.'

'You know that I'm married to the army.'

'Yes, but that doesn't impact on me. Just do your job and I'll be happy.'

'What do you want me to do?'

'Go back to what you were doing before. I think that I frightened Pam and I didn't mean to.'

'I think everybody looks up to you, and can't believe that you are here before everybody else and are last to leave. You never seem to have tea or coffee, and nobody has ever seen you eat anything. I don't know how you keep going.'

'It's all smoke and mirrors. Whatever I do or don't do, I am still here. I've been summoned to Karlsruhr next week. So I might not be here for much longer.'

'Jim, Mr James, if Erich Schneidling is not happy with you he will fire you without getting out of his chair. If he has invited you to see him, believe me, it really is important and has nothing to do with losing your job.'

'Ingrid, I don't really care whether he fires me or not, I would just go back to what I was doing before I came here. I don't need much of an excuse to just walk out the door and never come back.'

Ingrid just looked at me, and I think for the first time actually saw that I was only working there because Eric Schneidling had asked me. It was not for the money or the status. It was just because he had asked.

She came close and kissed my cheek, turned and left. I wondered what that was all about. I put it out of my mind, as I made my way to the stores to see what else had turned up. I needed a larger warehouse and would ask Erich about that when I saw him.

# CHAPTER NINE

## *Onwards and upwards*

The following Monday saw me take a company car to Luton Airport, to catch a cheap flight to Strasbourg, where I checked into the airport hotel. I had collected a hire car at the airport and first light saw me heading out of Strasbourg into Germany and on to Karlsruhr.

I had never been to the HQ building and was mightily impressed. In reception, I was expected and directed to a large meeting room. There were already other people there. When Erich Schneidling saw me, he came and shook my hand. 'Thank you for coming, Jim. We can talk after lunch. I have set aside an hour for you.'

I realised that Erich was a very busy man, sitting on top of an expanding empire reaching out across the world.

The meeting was an annual event, where all the heads of overseas operations came together for what could be used to compare notes and exchange ideas for expanding the business. What I didn't know was what was to follow. It was to get all the heads of overseas businesses to work harder, and Erich was cracking the whip. I had no idea why I was there other than to be another whipping boy.

The meeting ended and we all had lunch, which I just looked at and didn't eat. I just had a glass of water, wondering why I was there at all.

After lunch, Erich found me and took me by the arm, taking me to his office.

'Thank you for coming,' was his opening gambit. I waited for him to tell me the real reason I was there.

'I really want to thank you for sorting out the UK depot. We have several distributors interested in taking our franchise. I have whittled them down to five, with a sixth being processed as we speak. I have put our architects on to the contract so that all the outlets will have the AU corporate image.'

'How does that affect me?' I asked, wondering why I was only getting interested at this point of the process.

'Jim, you will have to supply all these outlets with parts, and also take on board the training of their mechanics.'

I had the picture in my mind instantly.

'Herr Schneidling, there are two things that come to mind. Firstly, I was going to ask you anyway, and that's the size of our stores in Fenny. It's not big enough and we need to train my guys so that we can pass on the training around the country.'

Erich just laughed. 'Yes, I had that covered. Find a new site and build your stores as quickly as possible. You find the land and our architects will do the rest. As for training, you need to make contact with our development team here in Karlsruhr to send all your staff, not altogether but in twos, and then roll out what is really required. There is one other item that you didn't grasp and which I really want you to do, and that is stamp your mark, the AU brand, on the agents, so that they not only look the part but become an extension of our empire.'

'You need to let me know who and where and when.'

'All in good time, I just wanted to tell you personally and ask if you would take this extra duty on for me and for the company.'

'Herr Schneidling, I would be glad to help you in any way that I can.'

'That's settled then. I think that you have turned the UK business around and are well above target and have set a high standard for everybody else, and I thank you for that.'

'I don't want thanks. I just want to see the operation work smoothly.'

'And you do. There was that other thing with Ingrid. I hope that you have settled that amicably. I don't like to see a stressed-out workforce.'

'How did you know about that?'

'I don't know how to tell you this without upsetting you, but she sends me a weekly report and it was mentioned.'

'That's the last report that you will ever get. Either she goes, no, I go. I resign here and now. You can sort out your own business without checking up on me. You can find somebody else to spy on.'

'There, I knew that I would upset you. I will tell her not to make any more reports on you or anybody else. I don't want you to leave in a fit of pique. It doesn't become you. Say you will stay with us.'

'I don't know why I should. You have deeply insulted me. I have always done my best for you, and this is how you treat me and probably everybody else.'

'No, I don't. Everybody was against me setting you on. I did it more or less to confound my critics. You are running the best depot outside Germany and most of them inside as well. I apologise for insulting you. It should never have happened. I can see that now, and would ask you again to reconsider your resignation.'

'I will sleep on it and tell you when I get back to Fenny. Now, if you will excuse me,' I said, as I turned and walked out of his office and the HQ building, driving back to the airport as quickly as I could.

Back in the UK, I had lots to think about, including did I really want this job. It wasn't the money or the prestige of being the boss in a multinational company. I had no idea why I wanted or even needed this, but somehow I did. I think that it was showing everybody that I had worth. The fact that I couldn't read or write or count or know the value of money, I had a skill that I was unable to define but I could organise and knew every part on every car that AU made. Did that have any value? Not to everybody, but to somebody in one organisation it was important, really important, and that somebody was trying to be my friend not to punish me or laugh at my inadequacies, but rely on me doing a good job and showing the end result as an example to the world. Yes, I needed this job to just achieve that.

Next morning, I was in the depot at my usual time of six a.m. and made the call half an hour later. Germany was ahead of us by an hour and Herr Schneidling was always early in his office. I was put straight through. I told him that I acted in haste and would like to continue working in Fenny. He was delighted, and would forward me a list of agents and a timetable of events that the PR people would pick up to take maximum advantage of a marketing opportunity. For the first time, I realised that there was an army of people and companies being used to promote the image of AU and I was just a small part of that machine. I felt privileged.

'Jim, I have a really big ask of you, and that is that I want you to sit in on the dealership agreement negotiations and sign the contract, when you are satisfied with it, on behalf of the company. Will you do that please?'

'You know how much I hate signing anything.'

'Yes, but have no fear. You will be surrounded by the best lawyers and if it's not right, they won't let you sign anything.'

'If I have your word, then I will.'

'Jim, you will be the face of AU in the UK. At each signing and depot opening I want you to be there. You don't have to do anything or say anything; just your presence will be enough.'

'What with that and organising the training, it looks as if I'm going to be busy. Can I come and have the first week of training with the mechanics? I need to be up to speed on all the new developments and take stock of all the additional spare parts we will need to carry.'

'Yes, we will arrange things around that.'

'Thank you. I think that I need to get that new parts department built, as I think we are about to get busier.'

'I have to thank you, Jim. You are proving me right in everything I give you, and all the doubting Thomases have shut up and are now looking to their own areas of the business to try to bring it up to your standard. Bye, Jim, give me a call anytime if anything at all troubles you.'

With that he hung up. I replaced the receiver of my telephone and looked around at the men coming in to work for the day. They were in their white overalls and started work immediately on the repairs from the previous day. In two hours, the workshops would be clear to start the servicing. It was all going well. I waited in my office for Ingrid to arrive.

She came in with two days' post in her hand. She looked apprehensively at me.

'Is everything alright, Mr James?'

'Yes, but you are to stop spying on me. There will be no more reporting to anybody behind my back. Is that understood?'

'Yes, I didn't want to do it but was told that I had to. Does Herr Schneidling know this?'

'It was Erich that told me. If it happens again, I will walk out of here and never return and you can take the responsibility for that. Now, that post can be given to the department managers to deal with and what's left you can give to Fred. We have other things to do. The first of which is a visit to the Local Authority Planning Department. I need a 100,000 square foot warehouse as close to here as I can get it. You can start by phoning round the estate agents to see what they have on their books. When you have done that, you need to call our lawyers, whoever they might be, to see where we are with signing up all the new franchises. I need to be at all the contract agreement meetings, wherever and whenever they turn up.'

'Will I be needed for that?'

'No, you will stay here and hold the fort while I'm away. I will also be going back to Karlsruhr in the next couple of weeks with Bill Ellis and a couple of mechanics to get up to speed with the new models. Ingrid, we are about to start the real work, and it starts now.'

'Yes, Mr James.' She smiled and left me.

I telephoned the workshops and asked Bill Ellis to come to my office. He came immediately, wondering what the panic was. I quickly told him, and we sorted out a new rota for servicing vehicles so that we wouldn't be overloaded when we were three mechanics down. It wasn't that difficult, as it happened all the time around holiday periods. Bill would notify the men.

They would all need passports and time off to get them.

Things were moving in the right direction. My time in the parts department became less, although I did call in every morning when I was in the office. It was all going pretty much to schedule.

Meeting with the council went well as they wanted more jobs in the area, and since our depot was in an area earmarked for industrial development there appeared to be land readily available, all we had to do was buy the land. Ingrid found an estate agent who had such a piece of land, the purchase was put in the hands of our lawyers, the architects were notified and I signed the first document for and on behalf of AU (UK) Ltd. It was a stepping stone for the company and an even bigger one for me.

The week in Karlsruhr came and went. The mechanics were shown everything there was to know about the new models and while they were having various coffee and lunch breaks, I was in the parts department requisitioning everything we needed so that we would be ready for the launch, whenever that was. It was a long but interesting week and the guys were really impressed with the set-up and absolutely everything. In future, when they put on their monogrammed overalls, they would wear them with pride. At the end of the week, Erich Schneidling made an appearance and gave everybody, me included, a certificate of accomplishment. Before we left, he took me to his office and I gave him a briefing on where I was with everything before I left the office in Fenny. He was interested and pleased at my swift progress. We were bonding not only as work colleagues, but as true friends.

Back in Fenny, I was brought up to date by Ingrid. She had filled out my diary. I didn't know that I had one, but left things with her. The architects were coming in to see me with the plans for the new warehouse prior to going to planning, the first of the dealerships had been arranged for later in the week, in London somewhere. I stopped her there. 'Ingrid, you can go on arranging meetings and events, but only tell me one week in advance. I don't want to get overloaded with information.'

She smiled. 'Mr James, I think that you will take the company onwards and upwards. It is a privilege working with you.'

'That's nice of you to say so, but you and Erich Schneidling are pushing me in the direction the company wants to go.'

She again smiled, turned and left me wondering about having caught a tiger by the tail and not get devoured in the process. I went to the boiler house and had a cup of tea with the maintenance man, who was happy to tell me everything that had been going on in my absence. Evidently everybody was happy, maybe I could make them happier. I went back to call in to see Fred in accounts.

'Hello, Jim. I heard that you were back from foreign parts. You should go more often, we seem to get more done when you aren't around stopping us from working.'

'The way things are going, I will here, there and everywhere, but what I want you to do is to give all the staff a pay rise of ten per cent, and that includes you.'

'Well, I'm blowed. We don't have a salary review until the end of the year normally. Can I ask about this sudden rush of blood?'

'You can ask, but I have a feeling that between here and the end of the year we will all have to put more hours in. If there is any comment from Germany, you can tell them that it was my suggestion and they can make a contribution to my generosity. Basically, we are leading the field and the only way to stay ahead to incentivate the staff.'

'Do you want a pay rise as well?'

'No, not really. I don't know how much I'm paid. It all goes in the bank and I never see it. I get a slip of paper with lots of numbers on that I don't understand and that's about it. What I spend, I keep a receipt that I give to you and I get my money back. It's all a mystery to me but everybody else holds great store by it. Oh, and you can include the maintenance man on that list as well.'

'It's as good as done. Can I ask you to go away again, soon perhaps, and come back with a more generous outlook?'

'You can ask, but I don't think that you will get a reply.'

I left Fred to work out the new numbers.

For once I went to my desk and sat down. Leaning back, I contemplated what had happened in just a few short days. I had changed from being a 'hands on' manager to one that gave out instructions and delegated tasks to others to perform. I had moved up the management tree and I hadn't even realised it.

# CHAPTER TEN

## *A strange turn of events*

My reflective mood was interrupted by the visit from the architects. Ingrid showed them into my office, where they laid out the plans of the new proposed warehouse. It was just a square building with roads in and out and the location of the doors. My only input was to reduce the number of doors, as we needed the space inside the building. Two would be sufficient, one at each end of the building. They also had an office block outside. I scrapped that idea. They could put a two-storey office block inside the main building with electrical stores underneath and offices above. I wanted 40 feet inside the building, so that with extending forklift trucks we could make maximum use of the space. I don't know what the architects' views were. They just listened, made notes and then left.

Ingrid came in to see me. 'Is everything alright?' she asked.

'Why shouldn't it be?'

'No reason, I'm just pleased for you,' she said, as she sat or rather perched on the edge of my desk, as it was the first time that she had seen me sitting down.

'What else do you have for me?' I asked.

'There's a meeting in London on Friday. I will give you the details later. It will be going through the agency agreement. Do you need me there for that? If you do, I need to make arrangements regarding picking up the children from nursery.'

'That won't be necessary, but I would like you to get a copy of the agreement and read it to me before I go to the meeting.'

'Can I call them now?'

'Sure, why not? The telephone's there.' I stood up and went to the window to look out.

Ingrid called the switchboard and asked to be put through to the lawyers. She spoke to a secretary, who put a draft contract in the post. It was as easy as that. They would all probably be the same and only the names and dates changed. It was not difficult being on this side of the counter regarding contracts and not the other, as I found out to my cost.

Ingrid put the phone down and came to stand next to me, wondering what I was looking at. I wasn't looking at anything in particular, but thinking that I was now at the hub of a growing empire of places and people. It was a feeling of power rising through my veins that I had never experienced before.

'Is everything alright?' Ingrid asked, turning to look at me.

'Yes, I'm just seeing the business in a different light, that's all. It will take some getting used to.'

She linked her arm through mine. 'You will be fine. You have come a long way from being a traveller.'

'Maybe, but I think that I have just started on that journey to go further and I have no idea where that will lead, but I always have the choice of jumping off if I don't think that I can continue or do a good job.'

'I don't want you to "jump off", as you put it. I want you to stay here and I want to stay and work with you.'

I thought that she was being too familiar again. She was a married lady with two children and I didn't want this. I removed her hand from my arm.

'I'm sorry but sometimes I just want to hold you. It's to give me reassurance as much as to give you support.'

'Ingrid, I may seem a bit straight-laced, but I'm not. You know that I was tricked into signing on and while I was away, my childhood sweetheart married somebody else. I also fell in love with another girl, Rachel, just before I was dispatched to Wuppertal and then Hanover for four years. I wrote her my very first and only letter. She never replied. As much as I'm attracted to you, I am aware that you are already married and have a family to consider. I don't have a girlfriend, and apart from you I haven't met anybody since I've been back. Don't make this any harder for me than it is already.'

'Oh, Jim, I had no idea, but I am attracted to you. You are everything that Charles isn't. You are hard-working and courteous and considerate and lots of other things, and I can see the loneliness that you have in your life and I am touched by it. I will keep my distance and not impose myself on you. You are the best thing that has ever come my way and I don't want to lose it.'

'I think that you had best go back to your office.'

She reached up and kissed me on the cheek before she left. My God! What was I thinking?

While all this was happening at work, I was still doing a few odd jobs around the yard with other people's boats and engines. Dick had done a good job on Andy's boat and was looking to cruise off into the sunset, exploring the whole of the canal network, until I explained to him that 70ft boats were unable to go on canals that were only 60ft long. For a while he was disappointed, but there were still over 1,000 miles of canal and river to explore. I guessed that it would take two or three years to cover the entire system and his mood picked up.

The day of the maiden voyage, Andy turned up with his girlfriend and left his car at the yard while he set off into the sunset. He would probably make Weedon for his first port of call. There was a good pub there where he could get a meal and a few drinks. If he was unlucky, he would buy beer for an 'old boatie' who would spin him yarns of the canal. He arrived back late on Sunday to go take his girlfriend home. I guessed that they had fallen out over something and I never saw her again. He would need to meet a lass off the cut and not off the bank. They had different values and using the toilet next to the bed in the middle of the night put things into perspective, and there were no shops on the cut, other than where you could buy bread and milk. After that, he came and took his boat for extended cruising and I only saw him once in a while, when he was full of his adventures on the cut. I was pleased for him.

Regarding Jonny Smith and his horse, the vet came a couple more times and the horse got better. I walked him every day in the evening and on warm evenings I pushed him into the canal and he swam up and down a short length before I could get him out on the slipway where we launched the boats. After giving him a rub down, he looked a picture of health. I gave the vet's bill to the bank, who transferred the money from my account to the vet's. It didn't matter how much it cost, the horse had recovered and was fit and healthy on the diet of hay and oats that I fed him.

One day, I noticed a newly carved notch by the padlock on the gate. Jonny had been and left his mark. The stable was empty. The hay and oats had been taken with the horse. Everything was fine. On my cabin top were a brace of pheasants. It was a thank you in kind. I never saw Jonny ever again. He had his life of freedom and I was set on making a mark in the world of commerce.

Back at work, the contract signing for new dealerships was well under way. As each one signed up, our design team were busy giving the new outlets an AU makeover, complete with signs that lit up and flags. I was in attendance at each and every opening. We provided champagne – a sort of German variety rather than the real thing, but it went down well. Orders were coming in for new vehicles and I pushed up the standards required by AU to all the dealership outlets, using the Fenny depot as my model. They all needed a full range of spare parts and our order book was rapidly growing, so that we were receiving a large delivery more or less every day. The system I had put in place handled the extra load with ease and everything was running smoothly. I had no complaints from Karlsruhr, except through Bill Ellis, who told me that the factory sometimes couldn't keep up with the deliveries. I told him to keep pressing them for improved delivery dates that they must keep.

Then, one day, I had a surprise. I met Lieutenant Colonel Bridge coming in as I was going out. I stopped and opened the door for him.

'Good morning, Colonel, how can I help you today?'

'I've come to see about buying a car and would like to see the head man.'

*The cheeky bastard*, was my only thought. I caught the eye of the sales manager, who came across to me.

'Wilf, this is Lieutenant Colonel Bridge, who would like to buy a car.' I then turned to him and asked for his car keys, which he handed over, being surprised by my request. I left him with Wilf to look at new cars, with a message to Wilf. 'Don't let him go without seeing me first.'

Wilf took the message and I went to drive Bridge's Standard 8 round to the rear of the depot, where I gave the keys to the apprentice. 'Give him the works; full valet and clean.'

The apprentice took the keys. He knew exactly what to do. I returned to my office to wait for Bridge to be shown into my office. It was some time before the sales manager had released him, bringing him in to my office. This time the tables really were turned. I was sitting at the desk while he was standing before me, until I invited him to take a seat. I offered him tea or coffee. Coffee. Wilf got the message, and a few minutes later Ingrid brought him his coffee and promptly left.

'I say, I'm awfully sorry, I had no idea that you were the top man when I met you at the door.'

'It was an easy mistake to make, but only one apology?'

'I don't get your drift. Thank you for the coffee but I would rather like the keys back to my car, so that I can make a move. I'm sure that you are very busy.'

'We are never too busy to speak to customers, and even potential customers. So how's Rachel?'

He was rather surprised by my question. 'Rachel's fine. She's recently got engaged to a captain in the Ordnance Corps, who has potential of rising through the ranks. How do you know Rachel, was it at university?'

'No, before that. It was at Catterick. Tell me, how many men went through your camp while you were there? Was it thousands, tens of thousands or even hundreds of thousands, and how many do you actually remember?'

'Remember? Very few I'm afraid, we had intake after intake. We split the numbers with Aldershot, but I can't say that I remember any. None that come to mind anyway.'

'I bet you remember me.'

'You do seem rather familiar, but my memory is not what it used to be I'm afraid.'

'I'm Private James. I was the troublemaker you sent to the cookhouse and then to Germany for five years.'

'My God! It is you. I would never have guessed.'

'No guesswork required. You never saw through Corporal Hunter, who was bullying me, or trying to. I pulled him off Rachel while he was in the act of raping her and half buried him alive, with Rachel's help I might add. You regarded me as the village idiot but from where I'm sitting now, I think that the roles are reversed, and I can see now that you are the idiot that hid behind your rank, and for that matter still does. You can pick up your car keys at reception. I wouldn't sell you a car no matter how much you couldn't afford. Good day, *Mr* Bridge, and give my regards to Rachel.'

Bridge almost shot out of his chair, making his way to reception to collect his keys. It was rough justice in my eyes. He still hadn't apologised, and I had forgotten to get his address so that I could contact Rachel. She might just be living round the corner or a million miles away. I would never be able to find her. Damn. Revenge does mean that you dig two graves and I had just jumped into mine.

Ingrid came in to see me.

'Who was that, and are you alright?' she asked.

'I'm fine. That was the camp CO that sent me to the cookhouse in Wuppertal for five years, the bastard, and it was his daughter that I went and fell for.'

'Sounds like a modern-day Romeo and Juliet.'

'Yes, he gave me the glad tidings that she has just got engaged to a captain in the Ordnance.'

'What's his name? I might know him.'

'Didn't ask and don't really want to know. That's another missing piece in the jigsaw puzzle of my life that I have now found. I vented my anger on him as now the roles had been reversed. Was there anything particular you have for me?'

'Only this,' she said, as she came over to where I was sitting, put her arms around my neck, putting her lips on mine giving me a warm, gentle, reassuring kiss. 'That's her loss and not yours,' she whispered.

To my surprise, I returned her kiss and had my hand on her waist. She stood up, smiled and went back to her own office. I sat there just wiping my face, removing her lipstick. What was I thinking? I needed to put some distance between me and Ingrid, but I didn't know how. The how came a couple of weeks later, when I took a call from Karlsruhr.

Ingrid came into my office. 'Erich Schneidling is on the phone, he wants me to listen in.'

She put the phone onto loudspeaker.

'Jim's here, Herr Schneidling.'

'Good morning, Jim. We are having a press conference tomorrow in Geneva at the Hotel du Lac du Parc at eleven local time. I am asking all the heads of operations across Europe and anybody else who can get here for a briefing this evening, prior to the press conference tomorrow.

I want you here in Geneva as soon as possible. You need to pack a bag for two days and just come. Ingrid, you need to get Jim on the first flight from anywhere to here, and make sure that he's on it. A car will be at the airport to pick him up here. Can you both do that, please?'

'Whatever you say. I'm on my way,' I said, and looked at Ingrid.

'I will get that arranged and will call you back giving you flight details.'

'Thank you. I'll speak to you later.'

The phone went dead.

'That's sorted me out for the rest of the week,' I reflected, looking at Ingrid.

'I think that you need to go and pack a bag, and I'll take you to the airport to get your tickets. Don't forget your passport.'

'I will be back in an hour, which should give you enough time to sort out flights and times.'

I left Ingrid to sort out the details and took my bike and rode up to the yard. When I arrived there, the telephone was ringing. I parked the bike and wondered who it was. Hardly anybody had that number and I was intrigued. I went and answered the phone to stop its persistent ringing. It was Ingrid.

'Are you packed yet?' she asked.

'I've only just arrived back. What's the rush?'

'I have to get you to Heathrow as soon as possible. That's the rush. I will come to pick you up and we can go straight there.'

'How do you know where I live?'

'The address I have is number 1, Northampton Road, Cosgrove. I think that I won't get lost between here and Cosgrove.'

'I'll be ready by the time you get here,' I said, and put the telephone down, thinking that she knew more about me than I realised. I had no idea where she lived or anything about her domestic arrangements. I went to the boat and changed back into my suit and packed a couple of shirts and some underwear. I would travel light. I assumed that I would be able to scrub up at the hotel. I also found my passport and was ready at the gate when she arrived.

'Turn the car around and I'll lock the gates behind you,' I said, as a matter of fact.

'It's a boat yard!' she exclaimed.

'Why? Did you think that I lived on a luxury yacht or a pillared mansion?'

'I never gave it any thought. Put your bag in the boot.'

I did as she asked and locked the yard gates, and sat beside her as we drove off as quickly as we could down the M1, heading in the direction of Heathrow. She was a good driver and coming from Germany, she was used to high-speed driving and we made good time. At Heathrow, we parked in the short stay car park. Ingrid came with me and bought my ticket, and saw me to the check in. I turned away from the desk and Ingrid put her arm around my neck to kiss me.

'I hope all goes well, Jim. I'll meet you whenever you get back.'

I didn't know what to say or do, but went through security with Ingrid on my mind. The journey was over in what seemed like just a few minutes, and I was met by a chauffeur and limo who quickly deposited me at the hotel in Geneva.

# CHAPTER ELEVEN

*Confronting the world's press*

I had never been to Geneva before, but this was not a tourist trip and I wondered what the panic was all about. I soon found out. Erich had called a meeting for seven but he called me on the internal phone to make sure that I was OK. It was all very strange and mysterious.

At seven o'clock I found the meeting room that had been booked. I recognised a few of the other staff there, and on the stroke of seven the doors were locked and security guards placed outside. Whatever was going on, it was top secret. We didn't have long to wait for the anticipated announcement. It was Erich that made it.

'Thank you all for coming at short notice. The press conference tomorrow is to announce to the world that we are pulling out of racing, as from eleven o'clock tomorrow. That means all racing, be it Formula One, Two, TT and rallying. There was yet another fatal accident yesterday at Spa and we cannot continue dishing out death every weekend. This has been coming for some time and it is with regret to all our fans worldwide that we have taken this decision.'

There was stunned silence around the room. AU had been in motor sport from the earliest days and had won championships and titles worldwide. The business had been built on the success of racing.

'Since there are no questions, perhaps I can tell you about tomorrow. The world's press will be on hand. There will be no comments before, during or after the announcement. I will take a few questions from the floor, but it will not be a lengthy, drawn-out affair.'

I couldn't understand why I was there at all. Erich had made a decision and we all had to stick by that and he would tell the world, beginning and end of story. I then received the thunderbolt.

'Jim,' he said, looking directly at me, 'I want you to field any and all the questions that are raised in English. Your reporters have a knack of asking questions that have hidden meanings and I don't want to get caught out.'

I was in a state of shock that he had singled me out in this way. All I could say was that I would answer as best I could, having so little information to go on. Maybe that was just as well, as I wouldn't be able to lie about something that I knew nothing about.

Erich then went on to outline what it would mean to the racing team, stating that from here on they would be deployed on designing better cars, safer cars and that the racing drivers would be used for testing purposes, but that would be their choice as they were being released from their racing contracts forthwith. They hadn't been told that yet. In fact, none of the racing set-up had been told and they would find out the same time as everybody else.

The meeting broke up and we were all told to go to our rooms. Telephone our nearest and dearest, but not a word to anybody until the official announcement the following day.

I went back to my room and ordered a club sandwich and a pot of tea. I had a visit from Erich.

'Thank you for coming, Jim, and I'm sorry if I dropped that on you, but I think you and I think alike.'

'Erich, your English is better than mine. I have a strange accent that sometimes comes out.'

'Yes, I like that. You aren't part of the establishment and speak with openness and honesty. You do this for me and I will see that you rise further up the management tree. I need you next to me in the boardroom.'

'Erich, I don't know what that means. All I want to do is the best I can for you. You just have to ask and if I can't do the job, I will tell you and you can find somebody that can.'

'I respect your honesty,' he said, and left me to my sandwich.

That wasn't the end of the interruptions; I had a call from Ingrid.

'Jim, I was worried and needed to know that you were alright.'

'Ingrid, I'm fine. Can you phone around all the agents to put televisions in all the showrooms as well as at Fenny, and tune in to the news channel at ten local time?'

'Why, what's the news?'

'You don't expect me to tell you, do you? You will have to wait with the rest of the world. Erich will make a statement tomorrow at eleven local time.'

'I'm just pleased that you are fine, and I hope that whatever's been decided won't impact badly on us.'

'I don't think that it has anything to do with us, but who knows. There is nothing for you to worry about. I don't know when I'm coming back, hopefully I won't be here long and will get back to work as soon as possible.'

'Jim, I really do have feelings for you.'

'That's nice to know, but I think that you are still a married lady and I respect you. Now, I must let you go, and I will see you tomorrow or the day after, depending on how things work out here. I will let you know which plane I'm catching and hopefully you will meet me at the airport.'

'Jim, I will be there for you whatever time you get back.'

That was a call I didn't expect but I walked around my hotel room. It had a small balcony that looked out over lawns, down to the lake that was surrounded by mountains. It was the scene off a chocolate box and this was possibly the largest chocolate box in the whole world.

I didn't sleep well, and was up and walked out along the shoreline of the lake, wondering what the day had in store for me. I couldn't understand why Erich wanted me to answer the questions in English. With a bit of luck they would all be in German or French, which I couldn't understand or speak.

I returned to my room and put on my suit, shirt and tie. The army had given me the routine of making myself really presentable. I made my way downstairs to be met by Erich, who insisted that I went into the meeting room to sit next to him. The other executives were also seated at the top table and there were rows of microphones already set up, with the photo press gang at the front of all the reporters and the television and film cameras set up at the back and down the sides. The hall was full of people, possibly representing news media across the world.

At exactly eleven o'clock, Erich stood up to speak to the world's press in German. He thanked them for coming and more or less repeated what he had told us the evening before. The news came as a massive shock to the motor sport world as cameras clicked and reporters were on their feet, wanting to ask questions. The first two or three questions were in German, which Erich neatly deflected. There was then one in Italian that he also answered. It was about time up, and I thought I was getting off scot-free until I heard a question in English. It was from a motor sport magazine asking if this was a knee-jerk reaction to the recent accident at Spa. Erich looked in my direction. I nodded my acceptance and stood up and moved closer to the microphones.

'My name is Jim James, and I have been asked to answer questions asked in English. I thank you for your interest in AU taking the difficult decision to cease racing from immediate effect. To answer your question, this decision has been coming for some time. Nobody wants fatalities in any walk of life. We all know and love motor sport, and from earliest times there have been accidents, but losing a colleague and friend is hard to take and we do not want to put anybody in this sort of position ever again, so this was not a knee-jerk reaction, but enough is enough and we have collectively made this decision.'

I took a breath at this point and held up my hand to stop any further questions as I continued. 'Can I say, on a personal level, we are not against motor racing, we as a company, a caring company, with our employees' health and safety uppermost in our minds, can't continue in motor racing. As for our motor sport competitors, and that's what they are, they aren't the enemy but friends in a highly competitive environment, we wish them well and success in all that they are doing. As far as we are concerned, we are not making any of the team redundant, but all our efforts will be directed into making better and safer cars that are tested to destruction not on the race track but on our own test track. We need all that expertise and will redirect it. We will be in competition in the showrooms and not the race track.'

I sat down. Hoping that would be the end, but it wasn't. It only sparked another question about providing engines for racing cars. Again, I was up on my feet.

'An engine is just an engine. We put our engines into cars and trucks. If there is a buyer who wants an engine, whether it is used for a boat, a plane or a racing car that is their choice. As far as we are concerned, it would just be another commercial transaction.'

I returned to my seat only to find out more about me.

'Mr James, can we ask what your position is in the company?'

'You can ask, and I will tell you. I am head of the UK business and report directly back to Karlsruhr. I am English and this is a multicultural, multi-racial organisation which operates worldwide. Can I say that we have taken this decision with considerable concern as I'm sure that our many enthusiastic fans around the world will be disappointed not to see the AU marque on the podiums in future.'

'What are the company plans for returning to racing?'

The questions were now coming thick and fast.

'We have no plans to return to racing in the near future. This decision will stand until there is a change of safety within the sport and even then, we might never ever return.'

At that point, Erich interrupted. 'The press conference is over. We have nothing more to say on this subject.'

He stood up and took my arm as he left the room.

'That was not in our press release,' he said as he admonished me, 'but on reflection, it is exactly what I thought and I would thank you for your honesty. Now, you need to leave immediately. The press interest in you will be good for business in England so you must be prepared for the media attention. There is a car out the back waiting for you to go now. Do you have your passport with you?'

I nodded my assent. He shook my hand as he pushed me out of the service entrance.

'Jim, I will make sure that Ingrid meets you at the airport. Now just go, before the rat pack find you.'

I went out the back of the hotel where there was limo waiting for me, and I climbed in to be whisked away. Three hours later I was walking out of the arrivals hall, to see Ingrid all smiles, waiting for me. She put her arms around my neck and I took her in my arms as she greeted me with a warm welcoming kiss on the lips, which I returned. It was something that I had wanted to do from the moment I had first met her in my office. I was still full of adrenaline and this was just a natural release.

On the drive back to Cosgrove, Ingrid gave me the news that they had seen my little speech live as it happened, and then later excerpts on the midday news. I was a news item in my own right.

The miles back to Cosgrove passed all too quickly, and I was back at the yard, unlocking the gates to let Ingrid and the car in. I closed the gates as she parked and stepped out to look around.

'Where do you live?' she asked.

'Let me show you,' I said, as I unlocked the padlock on the butty back cabin doors and hatch. 'This is where I live. I was conceived here, born here and now live here. Would you like to come on board?'

'May I?'

I stood in the back well and offered my hand until we were standing side by side. I pushed the slide back and stepped down into the cabin using the coal box as a step. I turned round and offered her my hands to help her locate the step, which was difficult in high heels and tight skirt. She fell into my arms, which I put around her as I kissed her. To hell with my principles, she was a lovely desirable woman and she was here in my arms and our lips met with passion.

'Jim where do you sleep? This is so small.'

I pulled down the cross bed and rolled out the mattress and the pillow and covers. I sat on the bed, pulling her down to sit next to me before putting my arm around her to kiss her again. I stood up, closed the cabin doors and pulled the slide across, leaving just a sliver of light before turning back to look at Ingrid, who had taken off her coat. I took off my jacket and tie before lifting her leg to remove her shoe and then the other. I stepped out of my shoes as I lifted her legs, so that she was now lying on the bed and I lay alongside her as our legs and arms intertwined and our lips met in warm loving kisses. It was all spontaneous and was loving and affectionate.

'Make love to me, Jim.'

And I did, as we undressed each other, lying on the bed before getting under the covers, unclothed and passionate as we came together as one.

I had no idea how long we lay alongside each other. I was happy at being drained and at having fulfilled a long desire to make love to Ingrid. It wasn't just another shag as far as I was concerned, and I was certain that Ingrid had wanted this closeness for longer than I realised. She was still in my arms giving me little kisses on my lips and my chest. I stroked her hair.

'Jim, I don't know what you are thinking but I don't regret this afternoon and I don't want you to either.'

'I don't do regrets. I think that I've wanted to make love to you from the first moment I laid eyes on you, but being married with children was always a barrier to me. I don't know why I have succumbed now, other than I was overcome with loving desire.'

'Jim, you just ooze sex and you are more than I could ever have hoped for. I have loved you from afar for a very long time and would never be able to say no to your advances, but you never made any.'

'I don't know where we go from here, but I can't see you living here sharing my life and space.'

'I can't believe that you live here. It is so small and lovely and cosy. Some other time you need to show me everything and try not to just make love every minute, although that's an option as well.'

'What time do you have to be back?'

'My mother-in-law has the children, but I would like to get back to tuck them up in bed. I need to tell you that my marriage with Charles is as dead as the dodo. He has little or no interest in me but only uses the house as somewhere to come to have his meals provided and his laundry sorted out. I think that he has a mistress somewhere. He is often home late and occasionally, there is an urgent meeting that lasts into the early hours and he stays over in a hotel. He has little or no interest in the children and sees them only occasionally at weekends, that is when he is not playing golf somewhere.'

'You already know that I'm not happy having an affair with a married woman.'

'Yes, I know that, and am surprised that at last you have given yourself to me. I am so lucky. I can't imagine why you haven't already been snapped up by some desirable female.'

'Don't meet any, and I haven't given much thought to anything other than surviving and now working.'

She sat up in bed and looked around for her clothes. 'I don't suppose that you have a bathroom.'

'Not as such. I suppose when you come to live here with me, I will have to get one fitted. I'll get Dick on to it when I see him next. Dick works here on the yard sometimes.'

'Is that some sort proposal or have I missed something?'

'I don't think that you have missed anything. If you aren't happy where you are and have designs on me, then it just seems a natural progression. I've wanted you here in my arms and in my bed. Now that you are here, I don't see any reason why you shouldn't stay.'

'I have two children to consider.'

'They can stay here as well. I have the other boat. I was born here and so was my brother Bobby and we grew up well enough.'

'You have a brother! I had no idea. Does he live here with you?'

'No, he lives with Mom and Dad in Rickmansworth. He is married and now has two children. He works on the railway as a fireman.'

'Will I get to meet them?'

'I will invite them to our wedding.'

'Jim, two things: I'm still married, and you haven't proposed.'

'We have already had the honeymoon; the rest is just a formality.'

She burst out laughing. 'That's a proposal that I never expected, but when I am a free woman, you must ask me properly and hope that I say yes.'

She was now getting dressed, putting her bra back on and laughing as she turned to give me a kiss. She stood up as she finished dressing.

'I do need to get back. You need to let me out of the gates.'

I looked around to start getting dressed.

She was ready first and rested against the doorstep, watching me. She had seen my knife for the first time but didn't ask or make a comment. Instead, she gave me instructions for the following day.

'Jim, I've heard that the press are likely to show up at the showroom tomorrow to see you. Erich has suggested that you don't arrive early but leave it until about ten, and then turn up in your red convertible to make a grand entrance.'

'Ah, forever the showman. OK. I'll be suitably attired. Now, give me one more kiss, as it's likely to be some time before I get another.'

She put her arms around my neck and kissed me with passion one last time. I helped her off the boat and opened the gates as she drove off. I went back to the boat, wondering what I had in for supper. It might be another trip to the chip shop. I needed to get a better lifestyle.

# CHAPTER TWELVE

*Another surprise from the past*

It was still only Wednesday morning. I had lost track of time and what I was expected to be doing. Going to Geneva for an overnight stay had put my schedule completely out. If they wanted me to go in the AU convertible, I would. I took it out of the hovel and gave it some loving attention, until it was bright and shining as if it had just come off the production line, albeit twenty years later. I put on my best suit and then a great coat, together with a floppy fedora that would make an impression.

At the office, Ingrid had been correct, there was an army of photographers and camera men who must be TV and film newsreel people. I drew up to the front door and parked the red monster, switched off the engine and stepped out. I removed my great coat and hat, throwing them nonchalantly on to the back seat. I ignored the press corps and went to the front door. All my staff had lined up and applauded me as I walked in. There was shouting from the press. They wanted a statement or something. I turned to face them.

'Are you guys queuing up to buy cars?' I asked.

There was a ripple of laughter. I doubted that they could afford our cars.

'Have you anything to add to what you said in Geneva yesterday?'

'Yes, we make the best cars on the road today. That will only get better when we transfer all the racing revenues into new models. You are all welcome to test drive them.'

'Mr James, is this your car and what is it?'

I smiled. 'It certainly is my one and only car. It's a model K10 of 1935. AU only made eighteen of this model and this is the only remaining example. I found it and restored it myself. I think that one day it will end up in the museum, but until then you can sometimes see me driving around in it. I hope that you like it. I know I do. Now, gentlemen and ladies, I need to get on to do a day's work myself.'

I turned and went to my office, where Ingrid was waiting for me with a smile that said a thousand things.

'Jim, there's somebody to see you in your office. I think you will have a surprise.'

I had no idea what she was talking about. I went into the office and there standing in front of my desk was Rachel.

'Rachel, what are you doing here?' I asked in surprise.

'Waiting for you. It is you. I knew that it was. Jim, what's happened to the squaddie I met and fell in love with in Catterick?'

'Your father sent me to Wuppertal to peel spuds for five years. That's what happened. I wrote you a letter but never received a reply.'

'Oh, Jim, I did write you a reply, but it came back as it wasn't delivered. You had moved on.'

I pondered this fact. It was weeks before I moved from Wuppertal to Hanover. Rachel continued, almost without taking a breath. 'I was at uni in Nottingham and my parents didn't forward the letter on. It was only when I went home at the Christmas break that I got your letter. I wrote back straight away. I still have your letter and the one that was returned to me. Here it is, you can read it now.'

She looked in her bag and found the unopened letter with various markings stamped on it. I took the letter and put it unopened on the desk. I didn't know in my own mind whether I wanted to open the letter or not. I was afraid of what it might say.

We stood facing each other, lost for words.

'Aren't you going to open it?' Rachel at last found her voice.

'Later. Look, Rachel, this is not the best day to be here. I have half Fleet Street hanging round outside. How did you find me?'

'We were watching the news on TV last night and you came on at the AU press conference in Geneva. I thought I recognised you, and when Dad said that he had seen you a couple of weeks ago in Fenny and cursed that you were the squaddie that he had put on a charge to peel spuds in the cookhouse, I realised that it was you. I asked him where he had seen you and he told me here.'

'He called in, supposedly looking to buy a car. He doesn't have enough money to buy a car from me.'

'Jim, there's no point in being bitter. I guess he gave you no consideration or even a second thought.'

'Maybe, but he did remember me. All I wanted was an apology and I received nothing.'

Rachel took my hand. 'Jim, just because I have an idiot for a father, shouldn't stop you and I liking each other and loving each other.'

I relented. 'No, I guess not. My family aren't blessed with a great deal of sense either. Look, you can't stay here all day, have you taken time off work or what?'

'I work in an advertising agency in Northampton and have bunked off for the day with a migraine.'

'Can I see you again over the weekend perhaps, Saturday would be better than Sunday? Come in the morning and we can go for trip on the boat. I need to give it a run and was looking for an excuse.'

'Where do you live?'

'My boats are tied up at the boat yard in Cosgrove. That's just outside Stony, just off the Northampton Road.'

'Yes, Saturday would be good for me as well. What do I need to bring?'

'Just yourself. Being on the boat we will be away from the rat pack, telephones and every other form of interference.'

She came close and gave me a kiss. She was just as lovely as I remembered, and this was the girl that I had fallen in love with.

'Rachel, you need to go out the back way. I don't want you running the gamut of Fleet Street. That's where your car will be anyway. No car leaves here without being cleaned and valeted.'

Rachel smiled. 'Yes, Dad did mention that. I'll let myself out and look forward to seeing you on Saturday morning.'

I kissed her again and then she was gone. Damn! I still didn't know where she lived or any of her contact details. I could only hope that she turned up on Saturday.

My thoughts were interrupted by Ingrid, who came in and closed the door to confront me.

'She was the one, wasn't she?'

I just nodded.

'Will you be seeing her again?'

'Yes, we need to talk. What about I've no idea, but I need some sort of resolution of whether we still have feelings for each other or not.'

'What did she have to say, other than leaving her lipstick on your face?'

I found my handkerchief to wipe my mouth.

'Surprisingly very little. We have tentatively made arrangements to meet up this weekend, away from everything that's going on here. I feel as if the world has gone completely mad and I can't keep up with events.'

'Will she spend the whole weekend with you?'

'Ingrid, don't get jealous over something or nothing. I have no idea about anything just now.'

Ingrid just turned and left me. I had made love to her and then the love of my life turns up. I guess she had no idea about anything either.

I picked up Rachel's letter. I was unable to open it. How I wanted that envelope six, or was it seven years ago, but now I was unsure. I think that we had both changed, and I needed to know in what way and did we still have feelings for each other. I would find out on Saturday, but before that I had tiger by the tail with AU.

I took a call from Erich, who was pleased with everything. He had more column inches and television coverage than he ever imagined and there was no such thing as bad publicity, and this was good showing a concerning and considerate organisation regarding its customers' welfare.

I went in to see Ingrid, who didn't look up when I stood by her desk.

'Ingrid, get into work mode. We need to keep our personal lives out of the office. Now, what's my diary looking like for the rest of the week? I have lost track of everything.'

The telephone rang. Ingrid picked up the receiver and handed it to me.

'It's for you,' she said, handing me the handset.

I was Klaus, my Karlsruhr contact, asking about my next visit as he needed to show me the latest engine development. Unthinkingly, I answered him in German, making the necessary arrangements. At the end of the call I returned the handset to its cradle and turned my attention back to Ingrid.

'You never told me that you could speak German.'

'I thought you knew.'

'I read out all those letters to you, and I bet you can write in German as well.'

'Of course, I liked to hear your translation.'

'All this time and I never knew, never realised. You are more German than most Germans I've met.'

'That came from living and working as a German while I was serving my time on the Rhine. Now, what do you have for me?'

Ingrid was not angry, she was furious with me. She replied without looking up, speaking to me in German. *'You are in Leeds on Friday at a sales outlet opening. You need to be there by ten at the latest. That's it for this week.'*

I dropped my car keys on to her desk. 'Have my AU brought into the showroom and put on display. Driving around in that makes me more than obvious and right now I don't want that sort of exposure.'

*'You can take the car the company have provided for you, but you never seem to take out,'* was her reply.

I was beginning to think that from here on she would only speak to me in German.

'I had no idea that I had a company car, I've always gone on my old bike.'

*'Jim, your bike days are numbered. You need to get up to speed. If you rode your bike to Leeds, if you started now you still wouldn't make Leeds by ten o'clock on Friday.'*

'No, I guess you are right.'

I had really upset her by not telling her about my fluency in German, and making her not only read the letter in German but also give me a translation. I had never changed anything that she had done and was puzzled by this change in attitude.

I turned and left Ingrid to continue doing whatever she was doing. I had no idea and I never asked. I went into the workshops to see Bill Ellis, who had other mechanics working with our guys, teaching and training. Bill had everything sorted.

'Bill, which is my company car? I've only just found out that I have one.'

Bill laughed. 'What happened to your bike?'

'Nothing, I just can't pedal fast enough these days.'

We went from his office to see my company car sitting in the reserved spot in the car park. It was a top-of-the-range, latest model four-door saloon.

'This is it. You know all about it, and what you don't know I surely don't either. You will get an upgrade whenever a new model, top-of-the-range is launched, so you might get two or three different cars each year. We just recycle them through the showroom, discounted as being a demonstration vehicle.'

He dropped the keys into my hand. 'These are all yours.'

'Thanks.'

'Jim, we were all proud of you yesterday when you spoke on behalf of the firm. You have put us on the map.'

'I didn't see it like that. I was just thrown in the deep end; it was sink or swim.'

'As I said, you did us proud and I think everybody working here has told all and sundry that they not only know you personally, but regard you as an equal colleague and friend.'

'Bill, that's high praise, but don't expect me to live up to it. I'm really just a guy that likes engines.'

We walked back to the workshop, where I left Bill and went into the stores. They were now bulging at the seams. I explained that we would be getting a new warehouse serving the whole country and these stores would be just for servicing our own clients.

I took the manager back to my office, taking with me the architect's layout drawings. We sat down together and worked out a procedure for deliveries and also for dispatch. I started drawing on boxes where each model's parts would be kept, with special areas where parts for several models could be kept. This simple activity took the rest of the day and the best part of Thursday. I left it with the manager to order the forklift trucks and racking. Nothing would be transferred from our own stores. This would be a complete new operation.

It was late Thursday afternoon that I went to see Fred. I explained about the new warehouse that would be up and running within months, and how we needed to expand the workforce to run the operation. He just sat back and looked at me.

'What's the matter, Fred? Too much to do and no time to do it?'

'That's about right, Jim. Since you've been here things have done nothing but get bigger. You need to tell me how many men and when and what skills they need to have.'

'Fred, if you are stretched, why don't you get a couple of assistants to take care of the paperwork and everyday things, while you and I can put the world right over a cup of tea?'

'Now, that's the best suggestion I think I've ever heard you make. I will order extra packets of Typhoo tea more or less as we speak.'

I left Fred a happier man than when I went in.

I didn't see Ingrid again before I drove off in my company car, and then I was on the road early to get to Leeds and attend the official opening of the new showroom. Again, we had a large press gathering. It would all be good for business.

Before leaving, I shook hands with all the sales team and workshop guys. The girls in the office were all smiles as I took their hands in mine. It was a good PR job as well. I was late returning to the boat yard and tired from the driving. Maybe I needed a driver to ferry me around. No, I would do it myself and not eat into the company profits.

Saturday had been on my mind ever since Rachel had walked into my office and back into my life. I couldn't settle on anything. I was up and dressed for a day on the boat, and had it prepared and ready for going out. I had no idea whether Rachel would show up or not. I just hated this uncertainty and I had no way of contacting her. I would just have to have more patience and wait.

It was mid-morning when she drove into the yard, parked and stepped out of her small Mini. I went to greet her. Her arms were quickly around my neck as I held her to me, as I greeted her with an affectionate embrace and a lovely warm kiss on the lips. Suddenly, I realised that it was her affectionate nature that I had fallen for and had done so again.

'So this is your boat yard,' Rachel said, looking round at the hovels and lean-to sheds.

'Yes, and so are the boats. I live on the butty, *Ariadne*, and thought we could take the motor, *Leo*, up to Stoke Bruerne for a liquid lunch.'

'Sounds good to me. What do I need to do?'

'Just step on board and leave the rest to me.'

I helped her on to the motor, taking her by the hand. She looked lovely in the morning sunshine. She was wearing a summer dress with a cardigan. I thought that she might get cold on the return trip, but I had plenty of jumpers and fleecy jackets to keep her warm, and if necessary I could always light the stove.

The journey to Stoke was a three-mile-an-hour trip and I sat Rachel on the cabin roof with her legs dangling in the hatchway, while I stood in front of her, steering the boat from my brass tiller bar. She kicked off her shoes, which fell inside the cabin, and sitting back began cheekily running her feet up and down my inner thigh. The cheeky madam! I freed up one hand from the tiller and pulled her to me and kissed her. She got down from the cabin top to stand closer to me with her leg between mine, as we continued to kiss and caress each other. I had difficulty steering the boat, trying to avoid going up the bank or getting stuck in the reeds.

She wanted to have a go at steering the boat and we changed sides, and with a guiding hand I let her steer the boat. It went from one side of the canal to the other. Progress was slow, but fun. At the bottom of the Stoke locks, I tied up and we walked the short distance to the pub at the top of the locks. I ordered two beers and steak sandwiches for lunch and we sat outside. The canal pubs had never been like this when I was growing up, and were now beginning to cater for the general public. A couple of working boats went through and also a few cabin cruisers, the new era of canal enthusiasts. I had the opportunity of talking to Rachel.

'Tell me about university. What was that like?'

'It was hard work but lots of fun.'

'Did you manage to get a boyfriend while you were there?'

'Wouldn't you like to know?' she said, laughing but stopped when I replied.

'That's why I asked.'

She became serious. 'Not like that I didn't. In Nottingham there were lots of pretty girls and the boys could pick and choose, and they did. I wasn't short of dates but there was nothing serious.'

I guessed that she did have a good time and I wasn't on her mind at all.

Having raised the subject of previous liaisons, it was now Rachel's turn to quiz me. 'What about you and that girl, what was she called, Mary something or other?'

'Mary Lee. She married my chief rival for her affections while I was stationed over in Germany. I had just vanished off the face of the earth and she didn't wait, hoping for me to turn up.'

'Poor Jim, nothing seemed to go right for you. Haven't you had a girlfriend since? There are plenty of pretty girls working in your office.'

'Are there? I hadn't really noticed. I've really been too busy working 12-hour days to get the place up and running as I would like.'

We paused to finish our lunch.

'Would you like another drink?' I asked.

'No, that was fine, thank you.'

'Now tell me about your fiancé. I see that you have taken off your engagement ring again today, but the telltale indentation is still on your finger.'

'Yes, sorry, I didn't want it to get in the way of us getting together again.'

'So far it hasn't. Are you going to tell me, or do I have to start making wild assumptions?'

She composed herself, deciding how much or how little to tell me.

'After leaving uni, Dad's term in the army had come to an end and he retired together with his pension to a house here in Lavenham. Evidently, he grew up around there and went to Bedford School and then took a commission in the army. He just retired to where he grew up. I had been from one base to another and had no roots except the army. I found this job in marketing in Northampton and work there. It's only a small company and easy-going. I met Rupert at a regimental dinner. Mom couldn't go for some reason and Dad took me. Rupert was a captain and still is. He's an adjutant to some brigadier who is likely to go up the rankings even further, taking Rupert with him.'

'So when are you getting married?' This was the main question on my mind.

She became quiet and looked directly into my eyes. I think that she realised, possibly for the first time, that I was seriously in love with her and that she was about to break my heart. I waited for an answer.

She took a deep breath. 'The reason I can't come with you tomorrow or stay with you tonight, much as I want to do that, is because we are on church parade tomorrow when the first of the banns will be read. The answer to your question is within the month. Oh Jim, I just wish that it was you and not Rupert, and now I don't know what to do.'

'I know exactly what you have to do, and that is go and marry this man and forget me and everything that's happened between us. You have too much to lose being with me and I think my destiny lies with somebody else.'

Rachel's eyes filled with tears. She stood up. 'I need to go to the ladies.'

She left me to ponder on the situation. I had no idea what was going through her mind. She wasn't a virgin when I met her. She would have been seventeen and knew all about the MO giving out contraceptives, and maybe I had just been one of several men going through training that she had been with. Corporal Hunter knew all about that I was sure, and he was just taking his turn. Then at uni, she almost openly admitted that she had gone from one boy to another. Jim James, take a reality check. Let Rupert find out for himself about her whimsical past. She was no longer on my list of potential lovers.

She came back to the table with a forced smile on her lips and I walked her back to the boat. The return journey was a silent one. I had nothing to say to Rachel and she didn't know what or how to say anything to me. The love light between us had gone well and truly out.

Back at Cosgrove, I tied the boat up and helped Rachel off. It was almost an embarrassed parting.

'Will I see you again?' she asked.

'I don't think so and I don't think that I want a wedding invitation, but I wish you well in your new married life.'

She touched my arm, then turned away to drive her Mini out of the yard gates and out of my life forever. It was another closure.

I had little sleep that night, and Sunday lunch with the family was a regular event and I had little or nothing to say. They didn't have a television so they had not seen or heard of my performance in Germany, but I did make the local paper. Thankfully, they never had a newspaper as nobody in the family could read, and they all thought that I was still working in the storeroom. I didn't tell them otherwise.

# CHAPTER THIRTEEN

*Yet another romantic end*

Monday morning, I was back to my regular routine in the office. I needed to wait on the arrival of Ingrid to tell me my weekly rota and bring me up to date with what happened during my absence on Friday. She came in at her usual time and came to confront me.

'Morning,' was my greeting.

Ingrid didn't reply. She was still angry with me. I hoped that this anger would pass, and we could get back to having a good working relationship.

'What do I have on today and the rest of the week?'

*'Today you do whatever you do on Mondays. I've no idea. Tomorrow, you have a full day over in Bristol. There's another contract with a distributor that needs your signature. Next week, I have booked you out on a flight. You have probably forgotten that you are having a week there looking at the latest model. Do you want more?'*

She was still speaking to me in German!

'No, that's enough for me to be going on with.'

*'I hope that it doesn't interfere with your love life.'*

'I don't have a love life, as she is as good a married already.'

'You mean that girl you saw over the weekend was married?'

Ingrid was now back in English.

'No, she's getting married.'

'But you saw her over the weekend.'

'Yes, and that's what she told me. It was just closing another chapter in my life.'

'But she stayed with you over the weekend.'

'Ingrid, she didn't. She was at church on Sunday for the first reading of the banns. The woman in my life who's married is you.'

Ingrid just looked blankly at me. 'I'm getting jealous over nothing then.'

'How do you think I feel? I make love to you all afternoon and then you go home and sleep with your husband.'

'Jim, it's not what you think.'

'Ingrid, I don't think anything. I am being used again by you and everybody else. Get that ring off your finger, get rid of Charles, get a divorce then come and find me and I'll marry you and make an honest woman of you.'

'Is that the only proposal that I'm going to get from you?'

'Until you are a free woman, I'm not proposing anything.'

We just stood facing each other. Our thoughts were different but had the same conclusion.

'Jim, I don't think that I can work with you any more.'

I nodded my understanding.

'I will find you another girl out of the typing pool and will let you get on with your life.'

I gave the matter some thought. 'Ingrid, take a sabbatical, whatever that is. I will keep you on the payroll for at least six months, if not a year. You need to sort your life out and let me get on with mine.'

'Thank you. I didn't expect that, but I realised a long time ago what a lovely and thoughtful, loving man that you can be, and I'm glad that the others have passed up the chance of loving you. I think that I will return to Germany and stay with my parents and hope to sort my life out as best I can. It would be best if I didn't see you or have the possibility of seeing you. I just wish that you had told me that you're fluent in German, so that I could talk to you in my own language.'

I was going to say something, but she put her arm around my neck to give me what turned out to be a final kiss before leaving. She called in at the typing pool and then left the building. This was some Monday morning. I had not one, but two women walk out in me in two days. What sort of record is that?

I had one of the newer staff come and tentatively knock on my door.

'Come!'

The poor girl looked like a frightened rabbit as she put her head round the door and came in.

'Please, come in.'

She moved further into my office.

'I'm Jim James, you can call me Jim. I might be the boss here but it's only a title. I am human – a bad tempered human sometimes, and this is just one of those times.'

She just stood nervously looking at me, waiting for instructions I guessed.

'What's your name?' I asked.

'Mai.'

'I'm pleased to meet you. I hate paper. I don't want one sheet of paper left here in my office. If it has a place, then that's where it should be, but not here. Do you understand that?'

'Yes, I think so.'

'Mai, I think that you and I are going to get on just fine.'

She gave me a smile as she began to relax. I don't know what the other staff had told her about me, but relationships develop not on the word of a third person.

I thought for a moment and paced up and down the office. 'Please sit down. Anywhere, it doesn't matter.'

She sat on the chair opposite my desk and crossed her legs, waiting for more instructions. It gave me time to think and have another look at Mai.

She was in her early twenties and looked the part of a high-class secretary working in the UK HQ of a multinational corporation; dark skirt, white blouse and black tights and three-inch killer heel shoes. She sat with her notepad and pen in her well manicured hands with nail varnish matching her lipstick. Her dark hair fell naturally over her shoulders. The natural look must have cost a pretty penny.

'Tell me, Mai, do you speak German?'

'No, not really.'

'That's OK. I will read anything in German myself and they will have to read my reply in English. It's not a problem.'

There was silence as I sat on the edge of the desk in front of her, wondering what to do.

'Mr James, have I done anything wrong to annoy you?'

'Mai, in this office please call me Jim. No, seeing that you have a pen and pad, I take it that you can take dictation.'

'Yes, the company have a very strict test for any would-be secretary.'

'I suppose they have just put you in the typing pool at the beck and call of everybody.'

'Yes, that's about it. I am lucky getting this job.'

'Let's get this paper out of the way and we can all take a second breath.'

I handed her the pile of papers that Ingrid had left on my desk. 'Starting at the top, can you please read them to me?'

She read the first one, it was a letter to each of the heads of the depots under my remit. They were all in English and she read them without any trace of an accent.

'Mai, can you just sign them for me and put them in tonight's post? Thank you.'

'You want me to sign them on your behalf?'

'That's about it. Look, Mai, I think that I need to tell you that I have a great deal of difficulty in reading and writing. I was once tricked into signing a contract that took five years out of my life. So, I ask you to read everything and sign everything on my behalf. Understood?'

'Yes, perfectly, but how come somebody who can't read or write gets to be head of a company that is a branch of a multinational?'

At last she had found her voice.

'What does it matter? I have found my perfect job and I think that I have just found my perfect secretary.'

She bent her head and blushed.

We went on through the rest of the papers and Mai stood up to leave. 'I'll just get this in the post.'

'Mai, tomorrow I would like you to collect the post from my inbox, wherever that is, and bring it with your notepad and pen. Now I wish you good evening. There are a couple of things that I need to attend to.'

She gave me a nervous smile and left.

I went into the parts department, where they were setting up the spares for a new diesel engine. I seemed to spend hours in the parts department. I did return to my office before going back to the boat yard. Mai was waiting for me.

'What are you doing here? You should have left ages ago.'

'Mr James, Jim.'

'Yes?'

I sat on the edge of my desk, wondering what was on her mind.

'I just wanted to say thank you.'

'No thanks are warranted. As for your promotion, I think that Ingrid has left on a long-term sabbatical. That's nothing for you to worry about. You can take her desk in my outer office, starting tomorrow.'

'Mr James, Jim, you don't expect anything do you?'

'Yes, you to be here tomorrow morning and to do a good job for me and the company.'

'You will get that. I was just wondering whether you would like me to spend more time with you.'

'Delicately put.'

I took Mai's hands in mine and looked into her light blue eyes that just seemed to sparkle. 'Although I'm not married, I only want the best for you. Now, can I give you a ride home?'

She gave me a nervous smile and a nod of the head. She collected her coat and I met her outside, and gave her a ride to her apartment on the outskirts of Bletchley. At her apartment block she got out, and I drove back to the boat yard where I had a quiet evening and an early night, followed by a very early rise.

I had managed to catch Dick at the boat yard and asked him finish the full-length cabin on the *Ariadne*. There would be a separate bedroom, bathroom with shower, a coal stove for heating and wired for both mains electricity while the boat was on the yard and 12-volt circuitry should we ever to decide to go extended cruising with both boats. I would live on the motor while he was doing the work. I would pay him £2 an hour for as many hours and days as he wanted to work. I would reimburse him for all the materials he used. I knew that he would do a good job for me and I let him get on with it. I was certain in my own mind that Ingrid would come back to me and if she didn't nothing was lost, and I would remain single to get on with the rest of my life.

The rest of the week went well enough. It was an early start and late finish on Tuesday signing the contract. Again, there was still media interest. Back in the office, I cracked the whip with the architects to press on with building contracts and short-circuiting the Planning Authority. I signed the building contract on the Friday, after spending all morning with the lawyers going through the fine detail. I just needed for everybody to get a move on. I was becoming impatient, as I could see the orders increasing and the cars passing through our workshops being delivered to the other sales outlets was becoming a daily operation.

I had a request to attend a meeting in Karlsruhr the following week. I wondered what Germany had in store for me. Nobody else was involved, so it wasn't looking at new models. I would find out all too soon.

My flight to Strasbourg, and then a hire car to the factory in Karlsruhr, saw me arriving early on Monday morning and introducing myself to reception. I was initially shown a seat in the customer waiting area before being taken up to the first floor, where all the directors had their offices.

The girl escorting me spoke to me in German. *'Herr James, this is your office for when you are here in Karlsruhr.'*

'My office!'

*'Yes, it is the express wish of Herr Schneidling. Can I offer you a coffee? Herr Schneidling will be with you shortly.'*

*'Thank you. That would be very nice.'*

My God! Erich had put me down the corridor from his office. The realisation that he wanted me there more frequently became apparent. The question in my mind was, did I want that?

Coffee arrived, and I sat in one of the more comfortable chairs where a small seating area had been provided, as well as a large desk. I preferred the informality to drink my coffee.

Waiting for Erich gave me the chance to look around my office of oak, or was it pine panelling? It was all very Germanic and top-drawer. I was most impressed but had reservations as to why I had been given an office here, as I already had one in Fenny.

It was a few minutes later that Erich Schneidling came in. He was tall and elegant and moved with graceful ease, like a tiger searching out his prey. I guessed that I was his prey and he had already snared me.

'Jim, thank you for coming.'

'The pleasure is all mine. I don't know whether I should thank you for giving me an office here next to yours.'

'After your performance last week, I am putting you forward to become a director, here in Karlsruhr. It will take some time to make sure that you are voted on unanimously but I'm sure that it will happen, and then I'm giving you fair warning that you will be working here alongside me, which is where I need you.'

'Erich, I am happy and content working in the UK. I don't need to be elevated to a position that is possibly beyond me. What do they say: people are elevated to their level of incompetence?'

'Possibly, but if that's the case, I'm sure that you would come and tell me. Now, how are things in the UK?'

'Going well, I signed another dealership last week, and have put a rocket under the architects for the new parts warehouse and signed the building contract on Friday. Everything is in place to get up and running as soon as possible. I've given the builders three months to complete everything. To my surprise, they have agreed.'

Erich started laughing. 'You need to fire off a few rockets in other directions.'

'That's not what you have brought me here for; nor for you to show me my new office and drink coffee.'

'No, you are right. We are developing our commercial division. In the past we have just supplied chassis and engines to coach builders for buses and the like, but over on this side of the Channel our competitors are building vans and trucks and articulated tractor units. We have to keep up.'

'You want me to set up a commercial division in the UK.'

'Correct. Over the next few days that you are here, I want you to see the scale and size of our present operation and try to visualise where we are going with it. It will be exactly the same as the car set-up in the UK, but larger units to accommodate the larger vehicles.'

'How about financing it?'

'That's my problem. Keep Fred in the loop and he will report back to me. I will cover everything from here. You have nothing to worry about. Your sales are outstripping all other overseas outlets and are putting our export section under pressure. We are now working a double shift system just to keep up, and with your new dealerships coming online not only do we need that warehouse of yours, but we will be working round the clock just to keep up with demand. We are pleased that you have given us this problem.'

'So, what's the time scale for the commercial division?'

'We are working on a year, starting from now. You will need premises, fully operational workshops, yet another major part department and fully trained mechanics and sales staff, so that we are fully operational on the official launch date.'

'You already have that date?'

'Of course, but you can bring it forward if you like, but don't delay it.'

'As if I would. Do I have a minder to take me round?'

'Yes, Klaus is waiting now in reception. I hope that you two get on together. He is like you, a practical man who will be your main contact here.'

We both stood up. Erich shook my hand as he went back to his office and I found my way back to reception, where I met Klaus. It was Klaus who had called me in the office. We shook hands warmly. Just looking at each other, we knew that we could work as a team.

'Jim, my English is not so good.'

I interrupted him. *'There is no need. I am fluent in German.'*

*'An English that can speak German? I can't believe it.'*

From there on we only conversed in German, and I spent the whole week going round the commercial arm of the AU business, from diesel engines to the body works, from the development division to the road testing where the vehicles were tested to destruction. Everything was larger and reminded me of being back in Hanover when the tank transporters came in. I felt at home already.

Friday afternoon, I flew back to the UK. I was too late to call in at the office, but it would all be there on Monday. Dick had started work on the butty and I made myself comfortable in the back cabin on the *Leo*. I had a visit from a guy who wanted me to service his Armstrong engine that had failed. I would take the *Leo* out and tow his boat back to the yard, where I could find out what had stopped working and put it right. I was happy to be back home.

It was the following day that I caught the train down to see Mom and Dad. Dad was really in a bad way. He was a mere shadow from when I remembered him in his prime. Now he was racked with pain and he still refused to see the doctor. I think that he realised that he was beyond the best doctor in the world.

Bobby was still at work on the railways, which meant early starts and late finishes. Annie had Julie about to go to school and had a two-year-old running around her skirts. She was pleased to see me as I slipped her twenty Woodbines.

Mom insisted that I stayed to dinner, as sparse as it was.

I caught the train back to Wolverton and then on to the yard in Cosgrove.

It wasn't good news. My father died and we had the funeral. I met up with all my relatives. News had spread around faster than the *Nine O'Clock News*. There were uncles, aunts and cousins that I didn't know that I had. They filled the little house in Rickmansworth and were satisfied with drinks at the pub on the corner and plates of corned beef and cheese sandwiches with a dish of pickled onions.

It was later the following week that I had another late afternoon meeting with Mai. I had been in with Fred all afternoon, and upon returning to my office late afternoon Mai came in to see me.

'Mr James, I've typed all your letters that need signing.'

'Sign them and post them.'

'Don't you want to read them first?'

'No. I have no desire to read them.'

She gave me a weak smile. 'I am grateful to you for this job but don't know how to show it.'

'Posting the letters will do it for me.'

She left.

At the end of the day I went out to find my car. Everybody else had left for the night and I found Mai standing next to the car, evidently waiting for me.

'Jim…'

'Mai, is there anything wrong?'

'No, I was hoping that you give me a ride home.'

'With pleasure. Please get in.'

The drive to Bletchley was quite short in duration, but the traffic slowed my progress down.

'Mai, I'm getting hungry and would ask if I could buy you dinner. I guess you haven't eaten either.'

'No, you're right. My money doesn't go very far these days. Dinner would be most welcome.'

I went into the nearest town centre and pulled up outside the Post House, where we went into the dining room and were found a quiet table. The hotel was quiet for a Monday night and we ordered. I decided on a ribeye steak and fries, together with a glass of beer. Mai asked for the same and we nibbled on breadsticks while we waited.

'Tell me about yourself,' I asked while we were waiting.

'Nothing much to tell. Went to university to study English and couldn't get a job, so I took a secretarial course and managed to get a job in the typing pool, and I am really pleased to have moved up to being your secretary. Can I ask about you?'

'Don't really want this job, but while I'm here I want to make sure that I do it as best as I can, and that's about it.'

'I've just split up with my boyfriend and hoped that you had noticed me.'

'I've noticed you alright, but having lost the girl I fell in love with and also the woman I wanted to marry, all within 48 hours, I'm somewhat sensitive in the love stakes.'

'Looks as if we are both in the same boat. I never expected Gary, my boyfriend, to walk out on me for another older woman who could dote on him in goods and bedroom services.'

'Here's food. Enjoy.'

We did. I think that we were both hungry and conversation dried up while we were eating. It was when we had finished that our thoughts returned to our personal relationships, but not verbalising it.

'Would you like anything else?' I asked.

'No, I can give you coffee back in my apartment. That's about all that I've got in at the moment.'

'OK, let's go.'

I paid the bill for the meal and returned to the car to drive Mai back to her apartment.

'Jim, you are coming in for a coffee.'

Once inside her apartment she took off her shoes and went into her small kitchen. 'Make yourself at home.'

Her apartment was small. It was just a bedroom, bathroom, sitting room and kitchen–diner. I went into the sitting room and chose an easy chair as I looked around. She came in to see me as she took her jacket off. 'I told you to make yourself at home. I can't believe that you wear your jacket back home.'

I relented and removed my jacket and my tie as she came to sit opposite me.

'What sort of music do you like?'

'Don't know. I've not heard much, only the sing-song at the pub on a Saturday night. We didn't have a wireless and we didn't have any musical instruments.'

'You do say some funny things. I can't work out the circumstances of your family. Coffee won't be long.'

'Nothing much to tell. I was born to a canal family. We lived and worked on the boats going up and down the Grand Union and Oxford Canals and going in to Birmingham now and again.'

'Did you go to school?'

'No. Not really, that's why I'm not very good at reading and I find writing really difficult.'

'Why didn't you tell me? I just thought that you were a bit strange.'

'Not strange, just not schooled. I have difficulty counting as well.'

'But all those numbers on the stores...'

'I know my numbers but not how to count.'

She stood up and went to the kitchen, returning with two cups of coffee.

'Jim, I think that I owe you one massive apology. I had no idea. If I had, I would have helped you.'

'You did. You read everything so that I didn't have to. As for signing things, I was tricked into signing a form that put me in the army for five years.'

She handed me the coffee before sitting down, just looking at me. It was as if she had just seen me for the first time.

I drank the coffee. I stood up and put the empty cup down on the table.

'Thank you for the coffee.'

Mai stood up with me. 'Where are you going?'

'Back home.'

'Why don't you stay here with me?'

'Are you suggesting what I think you are?'

She came to me and put her arms around my neck. 'It's something that I've wanted ever since I started working for you.'

I put my arms around her waist to kiss her. 'Now I have to go home, and will see you in the office tomorrow.'

I found my shoes and jacket and put them on. I had another kiss from her at the door as I left. As much as I liked Mai, and she really was a pretty girl, work was work and that's where I put that blossoming relationship. I still had Ingrid on my mind and in my thoughts.

I returned to simple living. I caught the odd rabbit and the occasional pheasant, and generally lived off boiled vegetables with plenty of bread, bacon and eggs. It was almost a full-time job just existing on next to nothing. On Sundays I would go to see Mom and give her something to cook for Sunday lunch. It was hardly anything, but it was more than we ever used to have. She was getting used to not having Dad around and Bobby would never throw her out. I had no idea how she got on with Annie, who seemed to smoke her life away.

The days and weeks went past at an alarming rate. I paid another visit to the planning department at the council, telling them that I needed a 100,000 square foot workshop, with a test track and an even larger warehouse facility within easy reach of the Fenny UK headquarters. They fell over themselves to accommodate me. Land was purchased, and the architects set about drawing up the plans even before the other warehouse was complete. I had long discussions with Fred, drinking tea in my office as we tried to put a financial plan together that included recruiting staff to run the new project. We just guessed at how many people we would need and how long and where the training would be. It was all a guess, as we had no idea about anything.

I was still opening a new sales showroom, more or less one or sometimes two a week, and signing up yet another dealership. Everything was going well, or so I thought.

I called all the dealers together one day and gave them the news that AU were going into the commercial vehicle market and if they were interested in taking on that franchise, I was available to draw up the necessary contracts. They all wanted the expansion of their business more or less at the expense of AU. As if there was not enough to do, I set up a distribution network for when the launch was made.

I was well into this programme of work with the new car spares department up and running and the commercial arm being constructed when Ingrid came to see me at the boat yard.

As usual, I had somebody's diesel engine in bits on the workbench in one of the hovels when I heard a car pull up in the yard. There was a slamming of the car door and then the sound of it driving off. It was all very strange. I cleaned my hands with Swarfega and then washed them with soap and water to see who, if anybody, had come to visit me. As I said, it was Ingrid.

'Ingrid!'

She came over to me and slapped my face as hard as she could. 'You bastard.' She almost snarled at me, and then put her arms around my neck and kissed me with a passion. 'I love you.'

'Ingrid, I've always loved you,' I said, as I returned her affection that lasted goodness knows how long.

At last, we took stock of each other. I was in my dirty overalls and she was in a flowery summer dress, with just a hint of make-up and her hair longer but still very tidy.

'Ingrid, what are you doing here?'

'I've come to find my lover, in the hope that he will ask me to marry him.'

'What about you? Is Charles still part of your life?'

'Yes, in as much he is the father of my two children, but he is no longer my husband. I've managed to get a divorce. I was right, he was screwing a woman he worked with.'

I didn't really know what to say, but Ingrid hadn't finished. She put her hand in her pocket and showed me her wedding ring. With a sudden swift movement, she threw the ring into the canal.

I took her in my arms and kissed her with a release of my pent-up passion for her. 'It's against the law to throw things in the canal,' I advised her between kisses.

'I don't give a damn. I want him out of my life and you in it. God, I've missed you these past months.'

I held her at arm's length. 'Let me get out of these overalls, there is something that we have to do and there's no time like the present for doing it.'

'What's that, or do I have to guess?'

'Marry me, here and now,' I said, as I stepped out of my overalls.

'I don't understand…'

I took her hand. 'Just stand and wait there.'

I went first on the boat and took out two gold rings from the ticket drawer, and then into a workshop where I found a besom and laid it on the ground next to us. I needed to explain. 'These rings belonged to my grandparents and we can use these.'

'What have you mind?'

'We make a marriage vow to each other and then jump the broomstick. It's the canal way. My parents were married this way and so were my grandparents.'

'It's not legal.'

'What's legality got to do with anything? We both love each other, what else matters?'

'I suppose you are right.'

'Ingrid, will you marry me?'

'Oh Jim, I would love to.'

I took her left hand. 'Ingrid Hargreaves, with this ring, I thee wed, now and forever and forsake all others.'

I put my grandmother's ring on her finger. 'Now you,' I prompted.

She took my grandfather's ring and held my hand in hers.

'Jim James, with this ring, I thee wed, now and forever forsaking all others.'

She then put the ring on my finger.

I took her by the hand and together we jumped the broomstick. I then set fire to the besom, and left it burning while I took Ingrid on to the back cabin of the *Ariadne*.

'What's happening now?' Ingrid asked.

'We complete the marriage by making a baby. I was conceived in this way right here on this bed, and hopefully it will work for you and me.'

Touched by this, Ingrid clung to me with her arms around my neck, kissing me with tears rolling down her cheeks. It was some time before we actually got round to consummating the marriage, and it was dark when we sat up and eventually dressed.

'Where are the children?' I asked.

'With Charles's parents. I need to go back to them.'

'Ingrid, while you've been away, I've converted the butty into a liveable home. I think that I need to show you.'

I put the bed back into its cupboard and walked through into the main area of the boat. Dick had done a good job on the conversion and everything was ready for Ingrid and the children to move in with me. She clung to my side. 'When can we come?'

'Bring them over tomorrow. I need to see my mother tomorrow for Sunday lunch. It's a bit of a ritual but one that I don't want to miss. I would like you to come with me. You need to meet the rest of your new family.'

She gave me another hug. 'I can't believe that you asked me to marry you and I said yes and we jumped the broomstick all within a few minutes. You are such a romantic and I just love you.'

'I love you and always have. Now, I think that you have to go, and I have to come to terms with having a wife and an instant family.'

'Jim, they will love you. I think that, given the chance, every woman in the world would love you,' she said, as she rained kisses on me again.

I had Saturday evening to reflect on what I had done. I had no regrets and I was sure that Ingrid was the woman for me. She came back to the boat yard at Cosgrove on Sunday morning. Going to Rickmansworth was another shock, rather than a surprise, to Ingrid. I parked the car outside the terraced house and knocked on the door. It was answered by Annie.

'Jim! Why do you always surprise us and not tell us when you are coming? Mom, Jim's here.'

She opened the door to let Ingrid and the children into the hall before me. She stole a kiss on the cheek as I put a packet of twenty Woodbines in her hand. Mom came to the hall door and stopped when she saw Ingrid and the children.

'Mom, this is Ingrid. We jumped the broomstick yesterday,' I announced.

Mom went and gave Ingrid a hug and kiss on the cheek. 'You can call me Mom. That no-good son of mine should have told me and I would have been there.'

'Mom, we spent most of the time in bed,' I confessed.

'You are just like your father. He could never keep his hands off me. I hope that you will both be happy and give me more grandchildren.'

'Mom, that's just what I want. I love Jim, and want boys that he can be proud of and daughters that will adore him.'

'Come in and tell me all about yourself. You aren't from around these parts.'

Mom led Ingrid into the kitchen, where she filled the kettle to make a pot of tea. Bobby was sullen, and Annie not only had Poppy but a baby in her arms and on her breast, but she still had a cigarette between her lips.

We not only had Sunday lunch, but stayed for afternoon tea that went on into the evening. It was late when we took our leave and Ingrid held my free hand all the way back to Cosgrove from Ricky.

Our first night on the butty was everything that I thought that I wanted, and it was all right here. Ingrid's children thought that it was all an adventure, sleeping on a boat. I put them both together in the fore end cabin. They would be fine.

Monday morning, I went to the Registry Office in Newport Pagnell to obtain a Special Marriage Licence and on Saturday, I sent a car for Mom, Bobby and Annie so that they could witness the civil ceremony that was over in a matter of minutes, and we all went back to the boats at Cosgrove which were our real family home. Mom stayed with us to show Ingrid how to live on a boat, while Bobby and Annie returned to Rickmansworth. What Mom really wanted was to go back to the life she had known and loved, it was on the boats; our boats, where nobody would ever be able to make us leave. She would have her grandchildren around her and was finally happy.

At the first opportunity, I took Ingrid and the children to see their German grandparents. They had been surprised how quickly Ingrid had remarried, and were even more surprised that she had married an Englishman that could speak fluent German. They were full of questions to which we really didn't have any answers.

Ingrid took control of my finances, for which I was grateful. I had no idea of the value of things and had never touched the money in my bank account. Evidently it was substantial, and eventually I pulled down all the hovels on the yard and build a house that could accommodate a growing family, and the boats were always there should I ever need them. I was well provided for.

As for me, I was propelled up to the boardroom and spend a few days each month in Karlsruhr and learnt the art of delegation, so that I continued with my double life of being a Director of AU, Monday to Friday, and a boatman at weekends living as I had been brought up. It seemed to be a perfect end, and it was.